PLANT LOCATION, LAYOUT, AND MAINTENANCE

THE IRWIN SERIES IN
OPERATIONS MANAGEMENT

EDITOR
HOWARD L. TIMMS
Indiana University

PLANT LOCATION, LAYOUT, AND MAINTENANCE

RUDDELL REED, JR., Ph.D., P.E.

Professor of Industrial Engineering
Purdue University

1967

Richard D. Irwin, Inc.

Homewood, Illinois

PREFACE

PLANT LOCATIONS, plant layouts, and maintenance systems are major cost areas for any plant, but we are only beginning to break the barrier to good analytical techniques for their evaluation. That reasonable solutions to the problems are possible is evidenced by the fact that systems operate in all these areas. How good these operating systems are, relative to what they could be, is questionable due to the lack of techniques to accurately define the optimum. Educational, business, and government groups are continually trying to improve problem definition and analysis techniques in order to identify the optimum solution. To date our available analytical models tend to be restricted to segments or skeletons of the total problem. Progress will be measured by the increase in effectiveness of problem definition; and by the replacement of procedural techniques that provide workable solutions with more rigorous analytical techniques which will permit optimum solutions. Initial optimum total-system solutions will likely be based upon a more or less static operating environment. Therefore, these solutions in turn must be followed by the development of methods sufficient to provide optimum solutions under dynamic conditions.

This volume presents, in the author's opinion, some of the better "state of the art" considerations and techniques. In each section the nature of the problem is discussed, as well as some general considerations necessary for resolution. In most cases procedural techniques for finding workable "good" answers are followed by analytical techniques that may not be applicable to the general problem but rather to a segment which can be more rigorously defined. These analytical techniques are usually based upon static conditions but may evaluate the influence of dynamic inputs. It is probable that future progress will occur either by increasing the size of the segment relative to the total problem, or by incorporating more dynamic influences, or both. Perhaps the greatest values of some of the "state of the art" analytical techniques are the avenues they open for future developments.

It must be kept in mind that plant location, plant layout, and maintenance are only subsystems of larger systems involving production, distribution, and other functions of the firm. Many dynamic influences, that must be considered in future developments, are in truth environmental influences relative to the subsystems at hand. They result from other subsystems within the firm and, in turn, from the firm's environment.

It is hoped that not only will this book provide a source of "state of the art" techniques; but that by bringing together procedural and analytical models it may serve as a springboard for the reader in the search for models that may provide optimum solutions, under dynamic conditions, to realistic and real-world problems.

Lafayette, Indiana   RUDDELL REED, JR.
April, 1967

TABLE OF CONTENTS

PART III. PLANT AND EQUIPMENT MAINTENANCE

BIBLIOGRAPHY

INDEX

PART I

Plant Location

PART I

Plant Locations

Chapter 1

—PLANT LOCATION
THEORY

THE PROBLEM of plant location can be defined as the determination of that location which, when considerating all factors, will provide minimum delivered-to-customer cost of the product(s) to be manufactured.[1]

A SHORT REVIEW OF THE DEVELOPMENT
OF ECONOMIC THEORY

Plant location theory can be considered to have passed through four phases:

1. The "least production cost site" phase where interest was concentrated on location factors directly affecting costs of production.
2. The "nearness of markets" phase. In this phase there were introduced more realistic concepts, such as the effects of uneven population, uneven resource distribution, imperfect competition, and the interdependence of firms within a multimarket economy.
3. The "profit maximization" phase. This phase stressed that the firm's optimum location was determined by the difference between total revenue and total cost.
4. The "least cost to customer" phase. This is similar to the profit maximization phase, but decision data related to delivered cost to customer. Greater emphasis on analytical models such as linear programming models and delivery time to customer.

---

[1] Factors, such as revenue earned and investment in a plant whose location is being determined, are taken into account in the long range planning and financial planning process as explained in Howard L. Timms, *Introduction to Operations Management* (Irwin Series in Operations Management [Homewood, Ill.: Richard D. Irwin, Inc., 1967]), chap. 5, and in William T. Morris, *The Capacity Decision System*, Irwin Series in Operations Management [Homewood, Ill.: Richard D. Irwin, Inc., 1967]), chaps. 3–5.

Relatively few attempts have been made to incorporate a theory of location into general economic theory. Although reference to the economics of location were made by Ricardo, Mills, and Marshall, most of the early work was done by German economists. The two classical works—Johann Heinrich von Thunen's *Der solierte Staat in Beziehung auf Landwirtschaft*, 3rd ed. (Berlin: Schumacher-Zarchlin, 1875); and Alfred Weber's *Über den Standort der Industrien* (Tübingen, 1909)—established the German influence.

Von Thunen studied a highly theoretical problem wherein he assumed a totally isolated economic system in which all nonessential aspects of a real situation had been eliminated. The analysis was based upon a Ricardian theory of rent. The study was concerned with the factors affecting location of different kinds of agricultural production to supply a consuming center or city. Wages were considered equal for all production locations. Thereby von Thunen found location to be a matter of minimizing the combined costs of rent and transportation. As did others of that period, von Thunen considered the problem under assumed condition of perfect competition. Under this assumption, price was determined by supply and demand. A location, which reduced the combined cost of rent and transportation below that of the marginal producer at a fixed demand, increased profit by an amount equal to the cost to the marginal producer minus the cost at the location considered. Therefore, a site which provided "least cost" of rent plus transportation was most desirable. It was assumed that any nominal wage differential was an element of the cost of land.

Von Thunen's work was primarily a study of agricultural production and rent. Weber, on the other hand, was specifically concerned with the location of industry. Procedurally the two approaches differ in that von Thunen assumed a location was given and the objective was to determine the type of product for that location. Weber, on the other hand, assumed the branch of industry known and sought to determine the proper location. It is interesting to note the two opposite procedures are both effective today. Political subdivisions, Chambers of Commerce, railroads, public utilities, and others who have a fixed site or region for location are faced, to a large extent, with determining the type of industry adaptable to the location (von Thunen approach). Attempts are then made to interest a firm involved in production of the selected product type in the location. The firm, on the other hand, having a determined product, seeks that location which, to it, appears to offer the desired potential for operations.

Weber, in his theory, considers three general location factors; the general regional factors of transportation cost and labor cost; and the general local factor of the agglomerating force.[2] He recognizes the factors of raw material

---

[2] Agglomerating forces are those forces which tend to cause industry to gather densely in a limited area: the factors or forces favoring urban location.

Deglomerating forces are those forces which tend to cause industry to scatter or to seek locations away from other industry: the factors or forces favoring rural location.

costs and fuel costs. However, these are grouped under transportation cost by assuming added raw material or fuel costs are equivalent to transportation costs for a location further from the consuming center.

Weber concludes that since the cost of transfer is the major significant factor, if the materials lose weight in conversion to product the location of production should be at the material source. On the other hand, if weight is gained in conversion location should be nearer the market. This conclusion as well as the agglomerating or deglomerating forces' effect continue to be significant in modern analysis.

The savings from agglomeration due to proximity to auxiliary industries, better markets, and economies of size are evaluated against high rent, the major factor encouraging deglomeration. The conclusion that labor is the vital force in agglomeration may be borne out by the tendency today toward deglomeration as labor mobility is increased. Weber defines a "labor coefficient" as the ratio betwen cost of labor per ton of product and the total weight of all goods transported. From this, he deduces a general rule: "When labor costs are varied, an industry deviates from its transport locations in proportion to the size of its labor coefficient."[3]

Weber excluded institutional and special factors in his analysis. However, the foundation of modern location theory lies in Weber's work. Transportation, labor, and weight differentials during processing continue to be major elements in modern location determination.

The second phase of the development of location theory, can be illustrated by the work of Hoover. Hoover[4] continues to consider the cost factors in location, but focuses on the role of product markets in the location process. Hoover tends to classify the cost factors under transportation factors and production factors. Costs of procurement and distribution are generally considered transportation costs, and institutional and agglomeration factors as production costs.

Hoover proposes that the "location relation of an industry to its customers (is) a system of market areas."[5] The assumption in this case is that the customers are scattered so that any one producer must sell to customers at a number of locations in order to survive. This is probably the most common location situation for manufacturing industries. Again, "The locational relation among producers competing for markets is generally one of mutual repulsion represented by the efforts of each seller to find a market where there is not too much competition."[6] Hoover points out that the sellers may be small and highly scattered, requiring the buyer to purchase from scattered locations in order to survive. In this case the locational relationship appears as a system of supply areas. "The formation of supply areas . . .

---

[3] Alfred Weber, *Theory of the Location of Industries,* trans. C. J. Friedrich (Chicago: University of Chicago Press, 1929).

[4] Edward M. Hoover, *The Location of Economic Activity* (New York: McGraw-Hill Book Co., 1958).

[5] *Ibid.*

[6] *Ibid.*

is . . . analogous to the formation of market areas." Although recognizing the necessity of certain industries (grain elevators are used as an example) to base location on supply areas, Hoover concentrated on product market locational analysis as the more common situation. Hoover's justification of selection of the product market condition as most common was found in a U.S. government report, *The Structure of the American Economy*, 1939, which showed 28 percent of the working population engaged in activities "close to resources," 48 percent in activities "close to consumers," and 24 percent "relatively footloose."[7]

Hoover recognizes the error in assuming transportation costs proportional to distance and points out that this nonproportionality causes the importance of transportation costs to decrease as transport distance increases.

Perhaps a more important contribution of Hoover is his recognition of capitalistic influences on location and bringing into consideration factors of taxation, utilities, banking, and public services. A major portion of *The Location of Economic Activity* (five chapters) is concerned with the effect of public policy on locational objectives. This last represents recognition of mid–20th century economic and political theory influences on location.

The last significant major contributor to development of economic location theory is Greenhut.[8] Greenhut divides location factors into four major classifications: (1) transportation costs, (2) processing costs, (3) the demand factor, and (4) cost reducing and revenue increasing factors. In addition to these four measurable factors, Greenhut recognizes the importance of personal factors in the final selection of the location. However, he concludes that such factors can be included in economic methodology by appliation of minimax principles between financial rewards and personal satisfactions.

Greenhut develops a general theory which is first presented as a nonmathematical formulation and later is structured mathematically.[9] The resulting general theory can be considered a profit maximization theory which combines both the cost and demand forces of earlier theorists into a single formulation. The maximum profit location, or "least real cost" location, is defined as "the site at which the spread between total receipts and total costs is the greatest."[10]

Greenhut states his general theory model as:[11]

$$1. \quad L = \phi(R - C)$$
$$2. \quad C = \phi(SR \times C_a)$$
$$3. \quad R = \phi(SR \times m)$$

[7] *Ibid.*
[8] M. L. Greenhut, *Plant Location in Theory and Practice* (Chapel Hill, N.C.: University of North Carolina Press, 1956).
[9] *Ibid.*
[10] *Ibid.*
[11] *Ibid.*

where L is the location; C is total cost; R is total revenue; SR is the sales radius, which by definition is proportional to sales: C_a is the average cost exclusive of freight; and m is the profit maximizing net mill price.

Greenhut considers a state of disequilibrium to exist when $m \lesseqqgtr C_a$ but $\triangle R = \triangle C$. When $m = C_a$ and $\triangle R = \triangle C$, locational equilibrium exists. Greenhut proposes that m or C_a can change, creating a state of disequilibrium; but new locations or relocations will cause a movement toward equilibrium conditions.

Greenhut's argument that his model represents modern practice as well as theory has some justification. However, the justification is in the attempt of the firm to locate in the manner of the general theory rather than on their accomplishment of this objective. Greenhut assumes profit maximization as the objective of management. Even personal factors are assumed capable of equation to this by the balancing of personal desires against lost profits to arrive at an equilibrium point at which there is realized the maximum value of the joint objective of the entrepreneur. However, Kaplan[12] and others have found that although profit is an objective of the firm, profit maximization most frequently is not.

Isard[13] and Moses[14] have also contributed to modern economic location theory. Although the techniques of handling the problem vary to some extent, Isard tends to follow the same basic philosophy as Hoover and Weber, arriving at a single best location based primarily upon transportation costs. Moses considers the interaction of demand with cost and although his formulation of the problem is somewhat different, it is similar to that of Greenhut. (Moses determines points of tangency of a system of isodemand curves to a system of isocost curves.) Both recognize location as dependent upon both cost and demand factors. Greenhut searches for maximized profit directly while Moses searches for minimum cost at a fixed level of investment which results in maximized profit. The two theories reach the same point, only the path of arrival differs.

The inability of the firm to satisfy the required inputs to general economic location theory models, the failure of the real world to remain in equilibrium, the variation in prime objectives of management, and the inability to quantitatively measure personal factors influencing location negate the direct application of the general theory models. Instead, the firm normally (1) designs or assumes a general approach to the problem, (2) establishes an incomplete set of factors affecting selection, (3) evaluates the factors, and (4) makes a decision based upon available data.

---

[12] A. D. H. Kaplan, J. B. Dirlam, and R. F. Lanzillotti, *Pricing in Big Business* (Washington, D.C.: The Brookings Institution, 1958).

[13] Walter Isard, *Location and Space Economy* (New York: John Wiley & Sons, Inc., 1956).

[14] Leon N. Moses, "Location and the Theory of Production," *Quarterly Journal of Economics*, Vol. 73 (May, 1958), pp. 259–272.

REVIEW QUESTIONS

1. What are the four phases of location theory?
2. What work on location theory can be considered the foundation of modern theory? When was this published?
3. Can you establish some likely reasons for the lateness of the development of location theory?
4. How does Greenhut's theory differ from that of earlier theorists?
5. How does Moses' approach to location decisions differ from Greenhut's?
6. What four basic steps does a firm normally follow in an actual location decision problem?

Chapter 2

PLANT LOCATION PRACTICE

A GENERAL THEORY of plant location may be of little value in treating a specific concrete problem encountered in the real world. A general theory may serve as a guide but must be extensively supplemented, or replaced, by techniques which are operational under the conditions of the specific case. It is necessary then to turn from plant location theory to plant location practice. Location is critical. Once established the location imposes restrictions on plant operations and management which limit effectiveness. The realizable limits of cost and profit are highly dependent upon facilities location. As stated by Stuckeman,[1] "Selecting a plant site is like selecting a wife—while it is possible to change later, the change may be both expensive and unpleasant." If general theories are inadequate, what approach can be taken to resolve the problem?

Location Principles

Before looking at approaches to the location study certain principles of good plant location need to be established.

1. Objectively determine the needs of the plant or other facility. Each alternative location provides its own peculiar combination of services and conditions. The prime objective is to select the site whose services and conditions best satisfies plant requirements. The degree of satisfaction can be determined only if needs are well defined.
2. Objectively determine the characteristics of the site which may affect the effectiveness of operations following location. As with plant needs, factual

---

[1] H. C. Stuckeman, "Community Evaluation in Site Selection," *Industrial Development,* Vol. 129, No. 5 (May, 1960), pp.–67.

and complete data is required. The selected location can only be as good as the plant and location data on which the decision is based.

3. Separate location studies from site studies.
4. Bring to bear the specific and different talents necessary to most effectively conduct or supplement the different phases of the problem.

The responsibility for decisions on location selection and facility planning rests with top management. However, top management must delegate the details to specialists including market researchers, economists, engineers, operations researchers, and perhaps financial analysts, sociologists, and others. The principal analyst must coordinate the activities of a diverse group, acting as a collector of facts and a maker of unbiased plans while delving into economics and probabilities to assure that the final result is both feasible and practical. The location, operation, and the organization constitute an integrated system each component of which affects and is in turn affected by the other components. It is imperative therefore that the principal coordinator apply rules and techniques of systems analysis and design in order to balance interactions to optimize the effectiveness of the complete system rather than of the components piecewise.

Making the Location Study

The location problem itself can be considered as a three-step problem:[2]

1. Choose the general territory or region.
2. Choose the particular community in the region.
3. Choose the specific plant site in the community.

Although the selection of the particular community is recognized as having a major influence on the success of operations, active participation of Chambers of Commerce, development commissions, public utilities, government units, and industrial parks provide the prospective new locationee immediate data on a variety of community sites. As a result, the site selection and community selection are often a simultaneous decision. The problem is therefore most frequently divided into two phases:

1. The selection of the general territory or region.
2. The selection of the community and plant site.

There may be an emerging necessity to consider location as a world problem rather than being regionalized nationally. The basic nature of the approach does not change, although economic factors of international scope rather than national must be included in the analysis.

Regional Analysis (General Territory). In economic location theory,

---

[2] This is an example of a sequential decision process in which there is feedback between the steps in the sequence. Therefore, the location selection process constitutes a decision system. For a general discussion of decision systems see Howard L. Timms, *Introduction of Operations Management* ([Irwin Series in Operations Management] [Homewood, Ill.: Richard D. Irwin, Inc., 1967]), chaps. 4 and 5.

we have seen the problem reduced to one of maximized profit by proper balancing of the factors of demand and cost. Yaseen[3] points out that all cost factors are regionally variable. He states: "In many industries, a differential of as much as 10 percent of total manufacturing and distribution costs can be effected simply by virtue of geography." Markets tend to exist as areas or regions rather than points or localities for an industrial producer. Major cities may act as the hub of a region, but increasing attention must be given to analyzing the impact of changes in policy at the state and national level which affects the location of the firm. In addition, arising influences due to interregional competition and cooperative regional economic development efforts of states, nations, or chambers of commerce must be considered.

When making the selection of a general territory or region, obtaining specific information about a given community or site can be a waste of time. Region selection calls for information of a more general nature. Long-range trends may be much more critical in the regional analysis than in the site analysis. The major factors in regional analysis are:

1. Market availability both from concentration and time to delivery standpoints.
2. Raw materials availability both present and future.
3. Transportation systems—variety, concentration, and rates.
4. Power—present and future—availability and cost.
5. Climatic influences—primarily affecting construction, heating and cooling costs, as well as personnel influences.
6. Labor and wages.
7. Taxation policies and other statutory influences.

A survey of 15 firms by Gary M. Leff of the School of Industrial Management, Georgia Institute of Technology,[4] provides information not only as to the factors in region selection but also as to why a firm establishes a new plant. The question was asked, "What prompts you to establish a new plant?" The answers can be grouped into three major classifications:

1. Product market conditions prompted 14 of the 15 companies. Production requirements had increased requiring added capacity. In 12 of the 14 instances, a change in the market pattern had also taken place, necessitating a new plant to satisfy a new customer area. The market factor is therefore composed of two components:
   a) A general increase in demand for the products of the firm.
   b) A shift in the distribution of markets, due most frequently to population shifts.
2. The need to lower costs of production was indicated by seven of the firms. Five of the firms were operating obsolete facilities resulting in excessive costs in a competitive market. Obsolescence forced relocation

---

[3] Leonard C. Yaseen, *Plant Location* (New York: American Research Council, 1960).
[4] Survey conducted during the spring and summer, 1962. Conclusions are the author's, using original survey documents.

of facilities. Excessive labor rates and power costs in present locations were also mentioned. Although only seven companies stated reduced costs of production as a major factor, costs were inherent in many of the other factors mentioned. At least 13 of the companies mentioned factors which indicated excessive production costs as a major element. Of the others, one was a young company with modern facilities and the other a company which had not built a new plant during the past 20 years.

3. A poor third as to factors influencing a decision to establish a new plant was labor. Four firms were prompted by labor conditions. Labor relations and costs influenced the new plant decision with labor relations appearing most frequently. It must be recognized, however, that if labor conditions necessitate a move, admission of the fact may cause militant labor reaction which could nullify any gains. Therefore, the firm may not admit the labor influence for fear of adverse labor reaction.

It is evident from studying the survey results that changes in the market for the product are the predominant reason for new plant establishment. A shifting in the geographical location of the new market, an increase in the market requirements, or the inability of present facilities to produce at competitive costs are the primary reasons a firm considers a new plant.

Mr. Leff's second question was: "How do you determine the region or area within which the new plant should be located?" The answers to this question were very diverse. However, four factors stand out. These four are markets, transportation, labor and wages, and raw materials. Two others—utilities and taxes—are also relatively prominent. If climate and living conditions are combined they provide the seventh most frequently mentioned factor.

In a tabulation of the frequency with which individual factors were mentioned, without subclassification by firm, labor and wage related factors had the highest cumulative frequency. This provides a false picture, however, since only 7 of the 15 companies mentioned labor as a major factor. However, when a firm considers labor as a major factor, there is a tendency to break it down into a number of facets: labor availability, labor cost, and labor relations. On the other hand, market is listed as a factor by 11 of the 15 firms but subdivided by only one. The factor was usually described either as "nearness to the market," or "within market area." Where labor is mentioned 17 times by 7 firms, market is mentioned 12 times by 11 firms. This would indicate that market is the more important of the two factors, but when labor is considered as a regional factor, heavy emphasis is placed upon it. It is also interesting to note that of the 11 firms mentioning markets, only 4 mentioned labor, indicating that when market is the predominant factor in location selection, labor may have little influence. On the other hand, 7 of the 11 firms listing markets also listed transportation as a major factor. Ten firms listed transportation as a major factor, making it second only to markets as to the number of firms influenced. Transportation facilities, cost, and time were considered for both the product and raw materials. In addition, at least one firm placed emphasis on facilities for executive and sales personnel travel.

The other of the four major factors mentioned—nearness to or the availability of raw materials—was mentioned by seven firms, the same number as listed labor. Taxes were listed by five firms and utilities by four.

The regional location factors list and the grouping of the data gathered by Leff are both short. In the actual analysis each of these major factors must be reduced to subfactors. The primary objective in the analysis will normally be cost minimization or profit maximization. However, to estimate cost and profits, other criteria of measurements may be necessary in evaluating certain subfactors. For example, under the major factor of power, questions relative to the method of power generation, availability of excess generating capacity, growth rate, service reliability, distributional system capacity, vulnerability to natural disasters, and interconnection with other utility systems need to be considered and analyzed in light of present and future growth demands. Technological factors as well as those of economics are present. Projection of future regional growth market demands, labor trends, long-range supply factors, and resultant costs accumulation are necessary.

Community and Site Selection

After determination of the desirable region the community and site within the region must be selected. The variety of factors, particularly those classed under cost and personal, is much more extensive for the site than for the region. In addition, evaluation of local attitudes and their effect on operations at the location must be considered. None of the regional factors already given, however, can be eliminated from a list used in the comparison of sites. In addition, as these factors as well as other factors are compared on a site basis, greater data detail relative to both technological and economic characteristics and effects must be obtained. Both the breadth and depth of factors affecting selection are extended. For this reason, more detailed discussion of location factors and their evaluation will be treated from the viewpoint of site selection.

Before considering site selection, it should be pointed out that the site selection cannot correct the errors of regional selection. If an inferior region is selected, the best site will not be realized, only the best within the regional boundaries previously defined. Except for engineering evaluation of physical input factors (i.e., power, water purity, natural hazards), the regional decision is primarily an economic decision based upon present and future economic or cost characteristics of the decision factors. It has been said that site selection is an engineering problem and regional selection an economic problem. If so, the result of the engineering selection of the site is highly dependent upon the economic selection of the region and both to be effective must consider sociological, political, and psychological influences.

Perhaps more mistakes in plant location are made because of considering only a fine site or attractive building, independent of economics, than for any other reason. An investigation of available specific sites should be made only after the community has been chosen that best combines the significant social and economic factors.

Except for a few large companies, plant location decisions are often once-in-a-lifetime affairs. The final objective is to select the best possible site over the projected life of the facility. *Factory*[5] asked 12 experts for examples of extreme cases of: (1) excessive costs due to poor site selection; (2) the two most important factors in site selection; and (3) the most common mistakes. The most common examples of extremely high cost resulted from: enticements of communities (four), poor transportation (three), inadequate required labor skills (three), lack of water and waste disposal facilities (two), and failure to conduct engineering tests at the site (two). The factor most often mentioned as one of the two most important was community attitude. The most common mistake was lack of sufficient data and evaluation before location. These results point toward the following steps in making a site selection:

1. Forecast future requirements by planned stages of development if applicable.
2. Develop and define location criteria.
3. Conduct site surveys which will measure the site by measures of the criteria.
   a) Look at past, present, and future trends.
   b) Tabulate the results in a manner which will permit comparison of one location to another in as objective a manner as feasible or reasonable.

The first problem arises in the selection of criteria, or as more often designated factors, for the location study. A number of factor checklists have been developed. These include a list proposed by *Industrial Development*[6] which includes the 10 major factors:

1. Markets (9-63).
2. Labor (18-128).
3. Materials and services (4-31).
4. Transportation (12-82).
5. Government and legislation (8-54).
6. Financing (5-40).
7. Water and waste disposal (10-72).
8. Power and fuel (5-38).
9. Community characteristics (26-181).
10. Individual sites (12-64).

[5] "Site Selection," *Factory*, Vol. 122, No. 5 (May, 1960), p. 197.
[6] "The factors for Expansion Planning," *Industrial Development*, Vol. 129, No. 11 (October, 1960), p. 64.

The numbers in parenthesis represent the number of subfactors and sub-subfactors under each of the major classifications. A total of 753 evaluation factors are represented. Any list of this type, in spite of its size, must be incomplete. Furthermore, it is unreasonable to consider all factors in the study of a single project. Cost and time will become prohibitive. *Factory*[7] proposed a list of 36 factors and 317 subfactors. *Modern Industry*[8] published another list including broad classifications of factors. None of these three large lists include all the factors of the others. Neither do they include any of the personal factors falling within Greenhut's third classification of location factors. Greenhut classifies location factors under three general groups: demand, cost, and personal.[9] Only the first two groups are included in the lists developed by practitioners. This is reasonable since the personal factors in location studies do not lend themselves to scientific or planned selection and evaluation. As a result, the nonpersonal factors must be evaluated for selected sites and the results balanced against the personal factor impressions of the plant locator and a decision reached based upon his balancing both the nonpersonal and personal factors. There is no evidence of a methodology of decision making jointly involving both type factors. However, sociological factors must be merged with economical and technlogical considerations. Such sociological factors as schools, churches, recreational facilities, and cultural activities, although generally recognized as factors in location selection, are difficult to evaluate directly by quantitative formulation. By necessity judgment must be exercised in estimating these effects on the technological and economic characteristics of the facility after it is established.

Dorothy A. Muncy, a consulting city planner of Washington, D.C., lists 11 yardsticks by which a community can measure itself or a plant can measure the community. These are, with some paraphrasing:[10]

1. Except in areas with a great deal of new residential construction the vacancy rate for tenant-occupied dwellings is normally between three and five percent. In older areas, a higher vacancy rate is a good indication of undesirable obsolescence.
2. If your community contains a smaller proportion of the young adult group (20 to 40 years) than the rest of the state, it is a clear indication that young people are seeking a livelihood elsewhere.
3. Is your community clearing out their blighted areas by using federal assistance under the urban renewal program?
4. Does the community have codes providing standards for light, heat,

---

[7] "Plant Site Selection Guide," *Factory Management and Maintenance*, Vol. 119, No. 5 (May, 1961), p. 180.

[8] John A. Shubin and Huxley Madeheim, *Plant Layout* (Englewood Cliffs, N.J.: Prentice-Hall, Inc., 1951).

[9] M. L. Greenhut, *Plant Location in Theory and Practice* (Chapel Hill, N.C.: University of North Carolina Press, 1956).

[10] "A Hard Boiled Look at Your Plant's Home Town," *Factory*, Vol. 123, No. 5 (May, 1961), p. 180.

ventilation, sanitation, structural safety, and occupancy? Do enforcement programs help to maintain code minimums?

5. Does the community have a staged program of major capital improvements? Are these realistically geared to financial capability?
6. What is the housing outlook for your future new employees? Do the economic statistics indicate a favorable trend in housing starts?
7. How about community facilities such as classrooms, hospital beds, parks, and so forth? What is the trend?
8. Is the water supply program being realistically handled? What about sewage and waste treatment; are these being programmed consistently with water supply?
9. Is there a shift in percentage of industrial land use compared with the other land use? How would these trends affect your long-range acquisition plans?
10. Is land use being realistically controlled by enlightened zoning policies?
11. What is the transportation and traffic picture? Are you bottlenecked and stifled for truck access? What about parking? Any hope for future relief by road and highway improvement?

Economic, sociological, and technological factors are interwoven in these 11 yardsticks. Error in any facet can affect efficiency of future operations of the firm.

It is apparent from the discussion that a wide variety of factors may be involved in community and site selection. It is not possible to establish a single list of factors applicable to all studies. Since many different and perhaps peculiar considerations may influence the proper site selection for a firm, the factors which enter into this choice, and the relative importance of each, will differ from one firm to another. It is impossible to put together a single set of factors and related techniques which will apply to any specific business or situation. This conclusion is inherently opposed to general theories proposed for plant location.

Although not proposed as conclusive, the following list represents the composite of major factors influencing 201 firms in site selection:

1. Transportation.
2. Labor supply.
3. Room for expansion.
4. Community attitude.
5. Opportunity for combining present facilities.
6. Nearness to supply.
7. Water supply.
8. Adequacy of transportation facilities and cost.
9. Pleasant living conditions.
10. Nearness to market.
11. Waste disposal.
12. Universities and higher education facilities.
13. Opportunity for highway advertising.
14. Topography of site.
15. Power supply.

16. Ability to retain present labor force.
17. Labor-management relations.
18. Fuel cost.
19. Labor rates.
20. Tax structure.
21. Schools (elementary and high).
22. Religious factors.
23. Availability of engineering and executive personnel.
24. Nearness to research facilities.
25. Commnity property offer.
26. Communications.
27. Climate.
28. Favorable experience of similar manufacturers.
29. Property costs.
30. Local government and taxation policies.

Location analysis in practice is considered primarily from the viewpoint of the firm. Review of factor lists, such as those above, is important only as they assist the individual firm to realize economic stability over the long run. Perhaps the most difficult phase of the location problem is selecting the factors to be considered by the firm.

Governmental Influences. In recent years, increasing attention has been given to policy and attitudes at the community, state, and national levels. State, regional, and local development commissions, as well as public and private development corporations, are attempting to attract new firms by offering tax, site, building or other direct incentives to the firm seeking a new location. For example, in 1961 *Business Week*[11] listed 33 states offering one or more of the following forms of assistance:

1. Property tax exemptions.
2. City and county bonds for facilities.
3. State financial assistance.
4. State chartered private development corporations.

Pressure of competition with neighboring states or communities forces incentives to be offered. The result has been interregional and intraregional competition for new industry.

The increased competition between sites has resulted in increased data being available to the firm for decision making, as well as reduced building and operating costs. A danger exists, however. Community enticements may result in high costs at that location in the long run. Wining and dining of prospective plant officials is a legitimate state, county, or local expense.

REVIEW QUESTIONS

1. Why is a plant location study critical to the firm?

---

[11] "Hotter Bidding for New Plants," *Business Week* (December 16, 1961), pp. 126–130.

2. Who is responsible for site selection? What specialists may be called upon to assist in the process?

3. What are the three steps in the location problem? The most frequent two phases of the actual study?

4. What effect may geography have on distribution cost according to Yaseen? Discuss some possible causes of this condition.

5. Discuss the factors affecting the selection of the region for the location of the firm.

6. In the location survey data gathered by Leff, no mention is made of profit. Why then does the author, following this list, consider profit maximization as a primary objective in analysis?

7. The author indicates that economic, technological, and sociological factors all influence location. In what basic sequence would you expect these three factor types to be considered? What may happen to the relative importance of the three in the future?

8. Why is the establishment of a general list of location factors difficult, if not impossible?

9. How do governmental subdivisions tend to affect or influence location decisions?

Chapter 3

MAKING THE
LOCATION EVALUATION

As NOTED in Chapters 1 and 2 the objective in plant location is to select that location which will either maximize profits or minimize cost of product delivered to customer or both. To accomplish either or both objectives completely requires that cost values be assignable to all factors of a location which influence cost and/or profit. Two conditions usually prevent the analyst's ability to accomplish this: (1) it is very unlikely that all affecting factors for all considered locations can be identified, and (2) once identified, many of the factors—particularly those of a sociological type—do not permit direct assignment of costs.

If costs and profits were assignable to all factors, the location problem would be one of summarizing for each location and selecting the optimum location based upon results. This would be a purely quantitative evaluation. Since these costs and profits are normally incomplete and assignable only to a portion of the factors, the situation usually reduces to separate evaluation of the cost factor list and the noncost factor list followed by subjective resolution of any resulting cost versus noncost decision conflicts. The resolution of conflicting results from the separate list results in a final decision based upon the joint effects of the two studies' results. The evaluation of the noncost factors must be done by qualitative (subjective) or, at best semiquantitative (objective) methods. We first look at some of these methods and then at quantitative methods best adapted to the cost factor list.

QUALITATIVE AND SEMIQUANTITATIVE TECHNIQUES FOR EVALUATING NONCOST FACTORS[1]

Three subjective techniques sometimes used for plant location are:

---

[1] For additional discussion see Ruddell Reed, Jr., *Plant Layout* (Homewood, Ill.: Richard D. Irwin, Inc., 1961).

1. Industry precedence.
2. Preferential factor.
3. Dominant factor.

(1) Industry precedence occurs when a new facility is located in an area previously selected by similar industry. Although not stated, the inherent assumption is, "if the location was best for similar firms in the past it must be best for us now." No location study worthy of the name is carried out. (2) Preferential study factor usually involves a personal whim and therefore the location is dictated by a personal factor influencing the decision maker (not the analyst). The desire to live in Florida or California, for example, may override factors of cost or profit in making the final decision. This is seldom a good business decision method but probably more common than generally recognized in practice. (3) Dominant factor occurs when one factor dominates any further considerations. The preferential factor above may be permitted to dominate, for example, on an arbitrary basis. In a true dominant sense mining or petroleum drilling operations must be located at the mineral source. Therefore, the source is dominant over all factors. The decision in this case is simply to locate or not to locate at the source.

The above are noted because each occurs in practice. The more common situation requires more detailed analysis of multiple factors each of which can be evaluated relative to alternative locations and, in turn, the locations can be compared based upon the joint effects of the factors.

The choice of factors is as critical as the choice of an evaluation system using the factors. To develop the factor list it is probably better to over list initially rather than under list. Any insignificant factors will tend to drop out of the joint evaluation. To accomplish this list:

1. Survey published lists and develop a factor list based upon combination of the lists.
2. "Brainstorm" to add to the resultant published factor list any additional factors which may have peculiar influences on the location of the firm.
3. Finalize the list. It is likely that steps (1) and (2) will result in over-lapping, identical, or insignificant factors. Finalize the list by eliminating the excess factors which cannot influence the final decision. Use care at this step since it may be better to retain and consider a questionable factor rather than eliminate it from any future effects on the decision. (Correlation analysis may be used in finalizing the list.)

Although these factors will represent effects on operational costs and profits, direct evaluation in monetary units is impossible or, at best, extremely difficult with a high probability of significal error. To incorporate these factors in the final analysis, factor ranking and factor weight-rating systems may be used.[2]

---

[2] This is an example of the use of cardinal numbers to express ordinal values to aid quantitative analysis. See the discussion of weighting in quantitative analysis in Howard L. Timms, *Introduction to Operations Management* (Irwin Series in Operations Management [Homewood, Ill.: Richard D. Irwin, Inc., 1967]), chap. 3.

Ranking may be conducted on an overall location or individual factor basis. In either case, no comparative relationship for values within the factor other than position in the list is established. A location is either better than or worse than another for the particular factor. Ranking is therefore largely unsatisfactory. By weighting factors and rating locations against these weights, a semiquantitative comparison of locations is possible.[3]

As a technique of location evaluation, the rating scale has much the same purpose as the cost comparison. However, it has an important advantage over the latter in that intangibles (those factors incapable of accurate monetary cost assignment) can be taken into account. Rating scales may be used to compare regions, communities, or sites against the factor and the factors may be either weighted or unweighted against each other. The rating techniques are an attempt to substitute a point value for a monetary value when monetary values are unobtainable or the cost of determination is prohibitive.

Four general rating methods are discernable in the literature. These are:

1. Assigning equal weights to all factors and evaluate each location along the factor scale.
2. Assigning variable weights to each of the factors and evaluating each location along the factor scale.
3. Assigning variable weights to each factor. The locations are then rated by a common scale for each factor. The location point assignment for the factor is then obtained by multiplying the location rating for each factor by the factor weight.
4. Establish a subjective scale common to all factors. Assign points against the subjective scale for each factor. Rate the location against the subjective scale for each factor and assign the factor points of the subjective rating for each factor.

Examples of the above are:

1. A manufacturer of fabricated metal products selected 50 factors by which to rate 12 sites. Each site was assigned a rating of 0 to 10 points for each factor. The sum of the assigned factor points constituted the site rating by which it could be compared to other sites.
2. A refinery assigned the following comparative ratings to major factors:

> Fuels 330
> Power availability and reliability 200
> Labor climate 100
> Living conditions 100
> Transportation 50
> Water supply 10
> Climate 50
> Supplies 60
> Tax policies and laws 20
> Site 10

Each site was then rated against each factor and a point assignment of zero to the maximum factor value assigned. The sums of assigned points

---

[3] See Reed, *op. cit.*

for each site were then compared and that site with the maximum number of points selected.

3. Rating weights of from one to five were assigned to 10 factors as follows:

Labor climate 5
Community facilities 3
Site 1
Power availability and reliability 2
Tax plans 2
Residential housing 3
Distance from (city) 1
Available work force 2
Available commercial transportation 1
Available tooling and plating vendors 1

For each of the factors, the site could receive 0 to 10 points. The factor points assigned were then multiplied by the factor weight above to find the site factor value. The sum of the resulting site factor values were used to compare sites.

4. Five subjective ratings—very poor, poor, adequate, good, excellent— were selected to be used in evaluating each site for each factor. For each factor a value of zero was assigned adequate. Negative and positive relative worth weights were then assigned the subjective ratings below and above adequate for each factor. The range between minimum and maximum weights assigned a factor in effect weights that factor against all other factors in the equivalent manner of (3). For a mandatory factor, a value of NG (no good) was assigned the "very poor" rating. Locations were then rated by selecting the applicable subjective rating for each factor for each location, and the equivalent points of that subjective factor rating assigned the factor. The sum of these points for all factors constituted a location's rating. (One significant feature of this plan is the use of the NG value. A location receiving such a rating is immediately eliminated from further consideration. A similar mandatory factor unavailable at a location should be used to eliminate that location from further consideration under any of the above methods.) A section of a factor rating table for this system appears as follows:

	Very Poor	Poor	Adequate	Good	Excellent
Water supply	NG	−10	0	5	8
Appearance of site	−2	− 1	0	1	2

In most cases, no attempt is made to establish a direct relationship between the point value of the site and the cost values. Rather, this is left for management decision. The location analyst presents to management both the cost and the intangible data results, with possible alternative recommendations. If monetary values are assignable the factor should be handled as a cost factor and only the intangibles evaluated by a rating plan. This provides maximum data for management decision.

Although errors will exist in estimating future requirements and conditions, the use of any of the systems above will improve the probability of choosing the best location to meet the firm's requirements. It should be noted that since judgment is involved in the evaluation procedure that person best qualified should evaluate each factor.

PROFIT OR COST SUMMARY LOCATION EVALUATION TECHNIQUES

Tangible factors influencing location decisions may be evaluated by summing costs or profits for alternative locations. This consists of nothing more than listing those factors for which costs (or profits) can be estimated for each location and then comparing locations on the totals. Lists include factors such as:

Transportation costs.
  Incoming materials.
  Shipped goods.
Labor.
  Direct.
  Indirect.
Plant.
  Rent in equivalent investment recovery.
  Annual expense.
Taxes.
  Real estate.
  Personal property.
  Income.
Insurance.
  Workmen's compensation.
  Property.
  Inventory.
  Liability.
Electricity.
Gas.
Other fuels.
Water.

Although listing costs or profits by location may appear relatively simple, it can become quite difficult when comparing regions or sites which do not agree in their ability to serve identical markets. Not only may cost vary, but the potential market or sales by which to recover cost may differ. As an example, as a plant moves further from its major market center unit cost may be reduced, but the market potential is also reduced due to the inability of the firm to satisfy customer time of delivery requirements as well as firms located closer to the market. For this reason, some measure of the rate of return should be considered which requires profit as well as cost measurement.[4] The effect of location on market size and mix is often criticial, yet is largely overlooked in the literature relating to location

---

[4] For a full discussion see Gilbert A. Churchill, Jr., "Plant Location Analysis" (Ph.D. dissertation, Graduate School of Business, Indiana University, 1966).

analysis. The trend of modern industry to minimize inventory investment and expect delivery on tighter schedules dictates the effects of location on delivery ability and resultant sales levels be given greater emphasis than in the past.

To illustrate cost analysis, assume a plant producing a single product requiring four tons of basic raw material for each ton of product produced. Further, there are two sources of raw material, S_1 and S_2, two alternative locations under consideration L_1 and L_2. Also, the market is defined by four market centroids M_1, M_2, M_3, and M_4. (A market centroid is defined as a point within a marketing area which can be considered as the point of market concentration for that area. Use of a centroid reduces the variety of data in making the final cost analysis while maintaining true cost or profit effects.) These locations are illustrated in Figure 3–1.

FIGURE 3–1

Locations of Markets, Sources, and Plant Locations for Illustrative Example

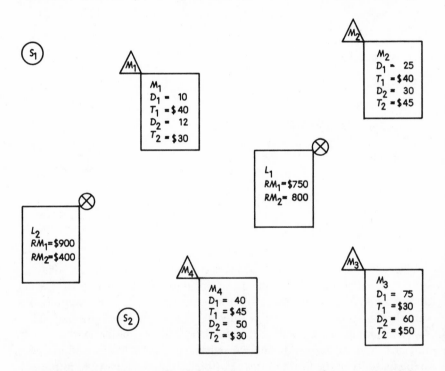

In Figure 3–1, RM_j is the delivered cost per ton of raw material from source j, D_i is the demand in tons and T_i the transportation cost per ton for the market if the plant is located at location, i. For simplicity, assume production costs of $400 per ton is the same for each location and the selling price in each market is $3800 per ton. We can then summarize the location data as in Table 3–1. Note the use of minimum cost source for each location.

TABLE 3–1
Costs and Profits at Locations 1 and 2

	Market 1			Market 2			Market 3			Market 4		
	D_i	Total Cost	Income	D_i	Total Cost	Income	D_i	Total Cost	Income	D_i	Total Cost	Income
Location 1 with RM_1*	10	$34,400	$38,000	40	$137,000	$152,000	75	$257,250	$285,000	40	$137,800	$152,000
Location 2 with RM_2†	12	$24,360	$45,600	30	$ 61,350	$114,000	60	$123,000	$228,000	50	$101,500	$190,000

* Summary: Total demand, 165 ton; total cost, $566,450; and total profit, $60,550.
† Summary: Total demand, 152 ton; total cost, $310,210; and total profit, $267,390.

Note that in the example costs are reduced per ton and profits significantly increased by the location providing the lower total demand under the assumption that only the minimum cost source of supply is used by each location. Note also that an analysis of this type may require a further management decision as to whether total dollar profit or rate of return on investment will be used in the final choice if one location provided maximum dollars and another a higher rate of return but lower total dollars.

Note also that since location may affect sales and thereby production levels, the specific design of the production process and thereby facilities for each location are likely to differ even during regional analysis. These differences are likely to become more pronounced as the decision reaches the site stage when topology, drainage, utility, construction, land costs, and other site factors enter the decision. Due to these interactions the decision maker is faced with a system analysis requiring decision to optimize the total rather than subsystems. This relationship is illustrated in Figure 3–2.

FIGURE 3–2
Subsystems Interactions Forming the Plant Planning System

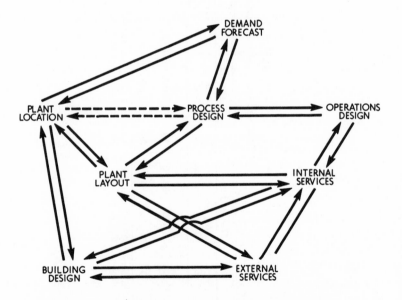

OPERATIONS RESEARCH TECHNIQUE MODELS FOR LOCATION EVALUATION

Most of the pure quantitative work which has been done relative to location studies has used some form of the transportation or assignment methods of linear programming. These in general, however, have been solutions to the problem of assigning "n" plants to "n" locations. The problem in this case is not one of selecting a location. The decision as to which locations are to be considered in the model has been determined prior to the model formulation. Furthermore, the number of locations must equal the number of plants to be located. In the normal situation of locating a single plant the model does not fit. The procedure may offer possibilities for long-range planning where several locations have been purchased and the question of when to use individual locations and what to produce at that location must be decided. This is, in fact, a location problem but of a special type.

Perhaps the most common type location problem considered for modeling is that of determining a profitable geographic location pattern for multiple warehouses of a firm. This problem may arise with either owned or leased warehouses. An examaple of this model is that of Baumol and Wolfe.[5] Baumol and Wolfe consider the location of the factory as known and fixed with known customer demands, factory to warehouse distances and costs, and warehouse to customer distances and costs. The objective of the problem is to minimize total delivery cost,

$$\Sigma_{i,j,k} C_{ijk}(X_{yk})$$

subject to:

$\Sigma_{yk} A_{yk} X_{yk} = Q_i$, i.e., all goods must be shipped out of the factory
$\Sigma_{ik} A_{ijk}(X_{yk}) = R_j$, i.e., no warehouse capacity can be exceeded
$\Sigma_{iy} X_{ijk} = S_k$, i.e., all customer demands must be met

where:

X_{ijk} = The quantity shipped from factory i via warehouse j to customer k
$C_{ijk}(X_{ijk})$ = Cost of this shipment
Q_i = Quantity shipped from plant i
R_j = Capacity of warehouse j
S_k = Quantity required at destination k
$A_{ijk}(X_{ijk})$ = The amount of inventory that will be held as a result of the flow X_{ijk}.

This basic formulation is a nonlinear program. However, it differs from the standard transportation problem by only three conditions: (a) the possible nonlinearity of the cost function, (b) the presence of warehouse capacity restraints, and (c) the necessity for a three-subscript rather than a two-subscript notation for the variables X_{ijk}. This is redudced to linearity by assuming (a) the objective function linear and (b) no warehouse capacity restraints due to use of public warehouses where only a portion of the space can be rented as necessary. Condition (c) above is made linear by assuming a least cost solution will involve shipment of all goods that go from factory i' to destination k' via that (those) warehouse(s) j' for which,[6]

---

[5] W. J. Baumol and P. Wolfe, "A Warehouse—Location Problem," *The Journal of the Operations Research Society of America,* Vol. 6, No. 2 (March-April, 1958), pp. 252–263.
[6] Superscript represents the optimal condition.

$$C_i'j'k' = \text{Min}_j C_{i'jk'}$$

Min_j is selected by inspection since a finite number of warehouses are involved.

The solution procedure is as follows:

1. For each pair i, k, of factory and customer find the least cost of shipment, ignoring warehouse loading charges and administrative costs. This involves selection of the least cost warehouse by inspection. Denote these factory to customer least costs C^0_{ik} and solve the linear programming problem to minimize $\Sigma_{ik} C^0_{ik} X_{ik}$.

2. For the warehouse assignments determined in (1), determine the warehouse loading and administrative charges. Add these charges to C^0_{ik} to obtain $C_{ik}{}^n$, the sum of shipment and total warehousing costs.

3. If the solution in (2) is the same as (1), the problem is solved. If not, determine new $C_{ik}{}^n$ costs for the new solution assignments and repeat (2). Continue until solution $(n-1)$ equals solution (n).

The technique of Baumol and Wolfe, or variations of it, have been used by industry to select warehouse locations. The decision has normally been the determination of the city in which to locate or rent warehouse space rather than selection of a specific site within the city.

Moore[7] reports a study in which correlation analysis was used to select those significant location factors affecting sales at a given location. Three hundred factors were initially selected as being variable in 51 cities. Simple correlation analysis reduced these to 74 factors. Multiple correlation analysis was then used to reduce the factors to 37 significant factors which when combined into a correlation equation gave a 0.98 correlation to sales per square mile.

Churchill[8] derives comprehensive models for the cost of producing a fixed quantity at a fixed location and uses this as a profit equation. Use is made of a production function of the general Cobb-Douglas form. Two current inputs to the production function and a current capital input, sensitivity, and limits of the relationships are developed. Although Churchill's theory appears to have merit, it has not been tested at this time.

Location analysts are faced with the dilemma that no fully satisfactory quantitative formulation of the location problem is available. To the author's knowledge the Baumol and Wolfe type model is the only one which has proven satisfactory in practice and this has been restricted to the location of distribution units served by the producing centers. Even in this case, the effects of factors associated with community attitude and labor stability must be estimated if they are to be incorporated in the model. Until a more inclusive, more widely applicable model or technique is developed, location decision will most likely tend to be made based upon qualitative or semiquantitative evaluations.

[7] James M. Moore, *Plant Layout and Design* (New York: The Macmillan Co., 1962).
[8] Gilbert A. Churchill, Jr., "Plant Location: A Theoretical Formulation" (Ph.D. dissertation, Graduate School of Business, Indiana University, 1966).

There has been no general economic theory of location directly adaptable to practice. The quantitative techniques and models which have been developed are restricted to limited conditions of application. This has forced industry to concern itself with the methodology rather than the theory. When determining the location of an activity technological, economic, and sociological factors as well as personal considerations of the entrepreneur enter into the problem. A systems approach to selection of the location is the best guarantee of a successful solution.[9]

In taking the systems approach, the principal analyst must rely heavily upon economic evaluation of alternatives. The selection of the geographical region for location is, for practical purposes, a problem of regional macroeconomics. The choice of a site requires satisfaction of technological requirements but alternative sites, after satisfying technological requirements, must be compared on the basis of economic effects on the operations of the firm. In the final analysis, the systems approach must lead to a decision based upon least cost or profit maximization principles, combining the processes of economic, sociological, and engineering analysis to satisfy joint firm objectives.

REVIEW QUESTIONS

1. Discuss why location normally cannot be selected on cost alone.
2. What is meant by a dominant factor? How and why may a dominant factor influence location?
3. How might a good list of factors to be considered in location analysis be arrived at?
4. List and distinguish between four general methods for rating noncost factors when making a location analysis.
5. How are the results of cost analysis and noncost analysis assimilated?
6. Compare a mandatory factor effect to a dominant factor effect in location analysis.
7. What is a market centroid? Why are these used in location analysis?
8. The data of Figure 3–1 does not include "time to deliver to customer." Would you expect this to influence the decision? Why or why not?
9. Why is location analysis a system analysis?
10. What difficulties have been encountered in applying pure quantitative techniques to plant location?

---

[9] A "systems approach" in analysis and decision making may be defined as a "decision system." For a general discussion of decision systems, see Timms, *op. cit.*, chap. 4.

PART II

Plant Layout

Chapter 4

THE PRODUCT
AND THE PROCESS

THE FACILITIES SYSTEM—GENERAL INTRODUCTION

THERE IS no finer example of a system than the combination of men, machines, and methods which constitute a manufacturing facility. All of the characteristics of a complex system are present including well-defined and ill-defined interactions whereby decisions relating to one element affect a significant portion of the total. The total facility system can in turn be subdivided into a number of major subsystems on the basis of materials input, product output, production processes and operations, material handling, plant services, and/or plant structures. In turn, the facilities system and its major subsystems must be compatible and integrated with the firm's system of organization, data systems, information systems, and decision systems which are necessary for operation of the modern firm. The physical facilities are at the heart of the industrial complex (see Figure 4–1). In the final analysis the total industrial system can be no better than the facilities which must produce the marketable product of required value to satisfy the customer. The effectiveness of the physical facilities available for production will tend to act as a constraint on the effectiveness of any other system or subsystem which may be designed for application in the firm's operations.

At the same time that facilities is critical to the effectiveness of other systems it is perhaps one of the most difficult to analyze, evaluate, and design in a rigorous manner. The variables involved are many and interactions are often very difficult if not impossible to define completely. Furthermore, facilities once established assume the characteristic of permanency and only to a limited extent are flexible enough to be adapted readily to dynamic future changes due to technological, economic, or market factors. To a large extent the firm is constrained by the facilities

FIGURE 4–1

Physical Facilities and the Industrial Complex

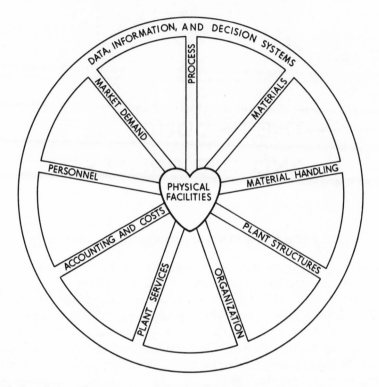

provided and the effectiveness of the facilities design in turn is constrained by the accuracy and adequacy of the objectives initially established.

The primary objectives of any facility is to produce a product mix of desired design in the required quantity of required quality at optimum cost. For facility design to meet this objective, input of product designs, production quantity requirements, and desired process is required. These inputs must be provided facilities planning by the product design, marketing, and process engineering functions. These data in turn must be supplemented by data or decisions from methods and time study, cost accounting, quality control or assurance, personnel (particularly as relates to job classification and wage rates), purchasing, and company management. In this text basic data and decision requirements will be noted, but only in a limited number of instances will any attention be given to means of obtaining them. Input in general will be derived by procedures or techniques presented in other publications in this series.

The decision processes employed in planning and designing the physical system are themselves a system in the conceptual sense. This is true because all operations of the firm are undertaken to serve a market defined by customer needs and desires. These in turn lead to product specifications, which in turn, within demand constraints, dictate the process design which must be jointly compatible with the plant design which in turn is dependent upon location, structural constraints, and arrangement. On the other hand, due to the constraints imposed the decision sequence also must run in the reverse direction providing feedback and adjustment toward compromises resulting in optimization of the total system which in the final analysis is the firm. The effects of the constraints may be economic, technological, or sociological. For instance, the initial concept of the process for producing certain product specification may not, in the course of completing the total design, be technologically, economically, or sociologically feasible or desirable resulting in a reiteration of the decision process from some earlier point. In general, the greater the number of iterations the closer the total system (firm) is to optimality. The problem is much too complex with today's tools to determine optimal, let alone derive a model to define input levels to attain optimum. We are therefore forced to analysis on a piece-wise basis. Industrial engineering and management science, as well as other groups, are concerned with research to devise models or simulations which will permit integration of larger segments of the total problem which will then permit closer approximation of total system optimization. The electronic computer must normally be used to simulate these decision systems, thereby permitting (economically) more iterations before necessitating a final decision. Until realistic, practical simulators are developed practitioners must be satisfied with relatively few iterations and often poorly defined interaction relationships, resulting in what are in all probability relatively nonoptimal systems. Therefore, the decision process relating to the design of the physical system and its effects on the total system is a dynamic closed loop decision process continuing throughout the existence of the firm.[1] The closed loop nature of the decision process is illustrated in Figure 4–2.

Input Data for Initial Facility Planning

Basic input data is a definition or set of specifications of the product(s) to be produced. These specifications are the output of final design (or designing for production) phase of the product planning function.[2] Although in many instances a class of products rather than specific designs are plannned, it is necessary that the required capacity of the different departments be based upon that department's loading. In general, this

---

[1] For a fuller discussion of these points, see Howard L. Timms, *Introduction to Operations Management* (Irwin Series in Operations Management [Homewood, Ill.: Richard D. Irwin, Inc., 1967]), chaps. 4–6.

[2] For a full treatment of the product planning function, see Lewis N. Goslin, *The Product Planning System* (Irwin Series in Operations Management [Homewood, Ill.: Richard D. Irwin, Inc., 1967]). The final design phase is explained in chap. 1.

FIGURE 4–2

The Physical System Loop

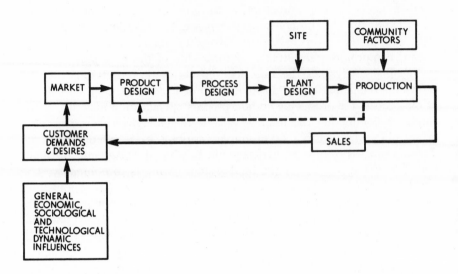

can be obtained by analyzing the production process required by individual products or by product groups. If product groups are used a basic production sequence for each group must be established. If deviation from the group process may occur either a new group must be established for the deviate or the significance of the deviation on group requirements evaluated and incorporated in the decision process. The determination of group requirements then becomes primarily the same problem as determination of single product requirements since it is dependent upon a single process assumed representative of the entire group. Our discussion therefore will be limited to the individual product, keeping in mind that if grouping is so broad as to include dissimilar processes, allowances for variation must be made or error will be introduced. Having established the product or group, it is necessary to translate product demands to facility requirements by means of some systematic procedure(s). These procedures constitute a decision system—a sequence of decision processes (subsystems) that are interrelated. These decision subsystems are:

1. Product drawings.
2. Assembly charts.[3]
3. Operation sheets.
4. Layout planning charts.

---

[3] These are specification sheets that record process planning decisions. For a full discussion see Gerald Nadler, *Work Systems: The IDEALS Concept* (Irwin Series in Operations Management [Homewood, Ill.: Richard D. Irwin, Inc., 1967]).

Product Drawings

Product drawings serve the function of identifying the item to be produced, or system output. It is the drawings which provide the basis for establishment of materials, machinery, and man requirements. Detail parts drawings are necessary for defining and planning the processing of the individual parts. However, from the plant planning standpoint the assembly drawing and the parts list developed from the detailed drawings provide the basic reference. The parts list (Figure 4–3) identifies the individual part by part number, references the parts drawing, identifies the part quantity for the final assembly, identifies material specifications, and provides for a make or buy decision on individual parts.

The parts list provides information necessary to plan storage and the process. For example, incoming inventory is dependent upon make or buy decisions (which should be based upon economics including balancing of production operations). Those parts to be made require storage provision of rough stores while "buy" parts create a requirement on finished parts stores.

A materials list (Figure 4–4) can be developed from the parts list. If the materials list includes information as to the production pieces quantity obtained per materials unit a direct tie-in can later be established between production lot size and inventory quantities. Knowledge of inventory policy will then permit improved planning of rough stores area and space allocation.

The assembly drawing if prepared as a schematic permits visualization of the relationship of individual parts in the final assembly (see Figure 4–5). For complex products schematic assembly drawings may be prepared for major subassemblies with a final assembly schematic which combines the subassemblies and individual parts required for their assembly into the final product.

The Assembly Chart

The assembly of parts into a final product can usually be accomplished in a variety of sequences. The determination of an optimum assembly pattern can be determined by use of precedence networks or precedence charts. These will be discussed later under line balancing. Let us assume for the present that an optimum assembly sequence has been established. The following discussion is applicable to any feasible assembly sequence.[4]

---

[4] The assembly chart, process chart, operations sheet, and other such documents that together specify the planned processes are more fully explained in *ibid*. However, layout considerations are taken into account in process planning. Conversely layout decision processes may feed back certain considerations, particularly constraints, that require revision in process specifications and even product specifications. In short the process planning and plant (layout) planning decision processes are highly interrelated, and as such constitute a decision system. See also Timms, *op. cit.*, chap. 5.

FIGURE 4–3

Parts List for Light-Duty Jack

Prepared by:__________________Checked by:__________________

Date:________________________Date:________________________

Part No.	*Part Name*	*Drwg. No.*	*Quantity Unit*	*Material*	*Size*	*Make or Buy*	*Remarks*
01	Side support #1	—	4	Cold–rolled SAE 1020 strip	8¾ × 1 × ³⁄₁₆	Make	2 holes
02	Side support #2	—	4	Cold–rolled SAE 1020 strip	8¾ × 1 × ³⁄₁₆	Make	3 holes
03	Side support #3	. . .	4	Cold–rolled SAE 1020 strip	6 × 1 × ³⁄₁₆	Make	—
04	Bottom and top rests . .	. . .	2	Cold–rolled SAE 1020 strip	4 × 3 × ⅛ 1 × 4 × ⅛	Make	—
05	Base	. . .	1	Cold–rolled SAE 1020 strip	8 × 3½ × ⅛	Make	. . .
06	Screw	. . .	1	SAE 1141 bar stock	¾″ × 12½	Make	. . .
07	⁵⁄₁₆″ pins . . .	. . .	4	SAE 1018 bar stock	⁵⁄₁₆ × 2½	Make	. . .
08	Socket	. . .	1	Cold–drawn SAE 1020 seamless	OD = 1D = ¾ L = 1½	Make	. . .
09	Tapped screw guide	. . .	1	SAE 1141 steel bar stock	OD = 1L = 1½ Tap = ⁹⁄₁₆	Make	. . .
10	Plain screw guide	. . .	1	SAE 1141 steel bar stock	OD = 1¼D = ⅞ L = 1½	Make	. . .
11	⁷⁄₁₆″ pins . . .	. . .	4	SAE 1018 bar stock	⁷⁄₁₆ × 1	Make	. . .
12	Crank section #1	. . .	1	SAE 1018 bar stock	⅜ × 30	Make	. . .
13	Crank section #2	. . .	1	SAE 1018 bar stock	⅜ × 20	Make	. . .
14	Crank hinge .	. . .	1	SAE 1020 cold–rolled strip	3⅝ × 1¾ × ¹⁄₁₆	Make	. . .
15	Journal bearing . .	. . .	1	SAE 1010 steel	OD = 1½ W = ½	Buy	. . .
16	Rivets	. . .	4	SAE 1018 steel	⅜	Buy	. . .
17	Stop pin . . .	. . .	1	SAE 1010 steel	³⁄₁₆ × 1	Buy	. . .
18	Hinge pins . .	. . .	2	SAE 1018 steel	⁵⁄₁₆ × ¹³⁄₁₆	Buy	. . .

It will be desirable to have production of the individual parts flow in such a manner as to minimize handling between their completion and their incorporation into subassemblies. In turn it is desirable to minimize

FIGURE 4-4
Materials List for Light-Duty Jack

Part No.	Material Specifications	Stock Size	Pieces/ Stock	% Waste	Weight	Unit Cost	Annual Cost
01	Cold–rolled SAE 1020 strip	$\frac{3}{16}'' \times 144'' \times 1''$	16	4%	2.04 lb./ft.^{2}	—	—
02	Cold–rolled SAE 1020 steel strip	$\frac{3}{16}'' \times 144'' \times 1''$	16	5%	2.04 lb./ft.^{2}	—	—
03	Cold–rolled SAE 1020 strip	$\frac{3}{16}'' \times 120'' \times 1''$	20	1%	2.04 lb./ft.^{2}	. . .	. . .
04	Cold–rolled SAE 1020 strip	$5'' \times 96'' \times \frac{1}{8}''$	24	18.5%	5.10 lb./ft.^{2}	. . .	. . .
05	Cold–rolled SAE 1020 strip	$3\frac{1}{2}'' \times 72'' \times \frac{1}{8}''$	20	6%	5.10 lb./ft.^{2}	. . .	. . .
07	SAE 1018 bar stock.	$\frac{5}{16}'' \times 120''$	48	0%	0.26 lb./ft.	. . .	. . .
06	SAE 1141 bar stock	$\frac{3}{4}'' \times 144''$	11	5%	1.50 lb./ft.^{2}	. . .	. . .
08	Cold–drawn SAE 1020.	$1''$ OD $\times 120''$	80	4%	1.24 lb./ft.	. . .	. . .
09	SAE 1141 bar stock	$1'' \times 120''$	80	18.7%	2.67 lb./ft.	. . .	. . .
11	SAE 1018 bar stock	$\frac{7}{16}'' \times 144''$	144	0%	0.50 lb./ft.	. . .	. . .
12	SAE 1018 bar stock	$\frac{3}{8}'' \times 120''$	4	0%	0.50 lb./ft.^{2}	. . .	. . .
13	SAE 1018 bar stock	$\frac{3}{8}'' \times 120''$	6	0%	0.50 lb./ft.^{2}	. . .	. . .
14	SAE 1020 Cold–rolled	$3\frac{5}{8}'' \times 72'' \times \frac{1}{16}$	41	4%	0.65 lb./ft.	. . .	. . .
10	SAE 1141 bar stock	$1\frac{1}{4}'' \times 120''$	80	19%	2.67 lb./ft.	. . .	. . .

handling of subassemblies prior to final assembly. The relationship of desirable in-plant parts flow is therefore directly related to the sequence in which parts are to be used in product assembly. In an idealized situation initial materials or parts will enter the plant, be processed in a straight line to produce piece parts, and in turn subassemblies and assemblies. If we now assume that processing of individual piece parts requires equal processing line length we would have the same schematic as the assembly chart of Figure 4–6, representing the sequence in which parts are combined to form subassemblies and these in turn combined to form final assemblies.

It follows from the above that if we develop an assembly chart we have established the corresponding desirable product production flow pattern. Whether the pattern is optimal or only feasible depends upon whether the chart represents an optimum or only a feasible assembly sequence.

FIGURE 4-5

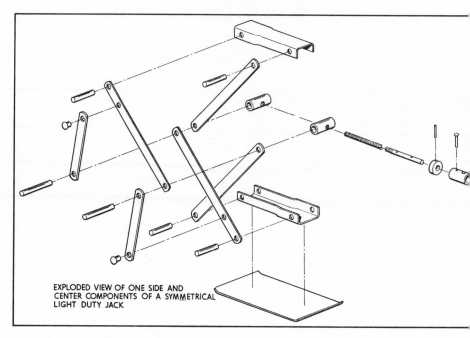

EXPLODED VIEW OF ONE SIDE AND
CENTER COMPONENTS OF A SYMMETRICAL
LIGHT DUTY JACK

Two further characteristics of the assembly chart should be noted. (1) Wrapping and packaging materials are included as parts. All too frequently these items are overlooked in planning even though they are in fact an integral and necessary part of the firm's product. (2) If we now superimpose upon the piece parts and subassembly flow lines those operations and inspections necessary to provide the piece part or subassembly we have established the schematic of an operation process chart. If we add to this the machine or assembly station on which the inspection or operation is to be performed and the time required we have defined not only processing requirements of the physical plant but the sequence in which these requirements will be accomplished (see Figure 4-7).

The development of assembly charts and operations process sheets are not a necessary requirement in layout planning. However, the time spent in their development will probably pay dividends as ready references for in-plant production sequence and physical flow relationships at later stages in the layout process.

Operations Sheets (Routing Sheets)

In order to plan any facility for the purpose of satisfying a production function two things must be known; what sequence of operations must be performed, and how long does each operation require. Time required in turn is dependent upon the method of performing the operation. In pro-

FIGURE 4-6

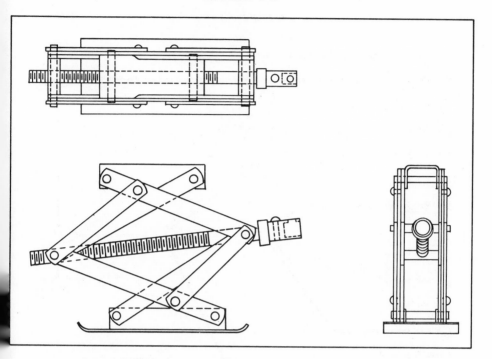

duction operations the operation sequence, method, and time is normally provided by the operation sheet such as that illustrated in Figure 4-8. Note that the operation sheet provides the operations sequence including inspections and assembly. The equipment to be used in performing the operation and the standard time required for the operation is shown. When necessary for clarification machine speeds, feeds, depth of cut, sketches of part's sections, and portions of the work station arrangement may be included as a part of, or attached to, the operations sheet.

It is recognized that the definition of operations and the method of performance, including machine selection, is dependent upon quantity produced and the combination of in-plant operations required. At the initial point in layout planning, however, there is probably no quantitative basis for making the final decision on machine selection and operation method. At this time it is sufficient to use those operation sheets prepared by process engineering based upon their best available information. Later in the planning cycle, when considering machine balance, attention may be given to the advisability of operation method changes.

The above discussion and in fact much to follow is in the language of discrete production wherein piece parts are progressively moving toward assembly of a final product. This reference is used because it can usually be more clearly defined in the physical sense. Processing type production and other "continuous" types are analogous in that a defined

FIGURE 4–7

Assembly Chart

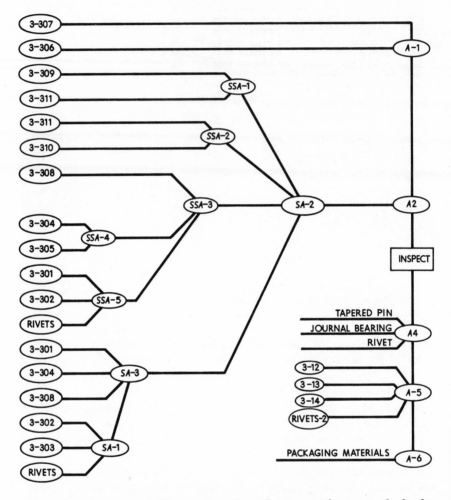

stepwise process exists. The variety of production within a single facility is normally less but volume per product greater than in the piece part type process. As a result of reduced variety, interaction between conflicting demands on a facility unit by competing products is reduced. Therefore, the piece part process represents the more complex problem in the general sense. We will look at line balancing for the continuous case later.

In service type production, such as paperwork flow in banks or insurance offices, individual forms or information pieces are analogous to piece parts. Their collation to master files analogous to product assembly. Operation times, storages, and inspections in the paper work processing also exist. The flow diagram serves the function of the operation-process chart and a complete analogy exists. As a result techniques or methods designed

FIGURE 4-8

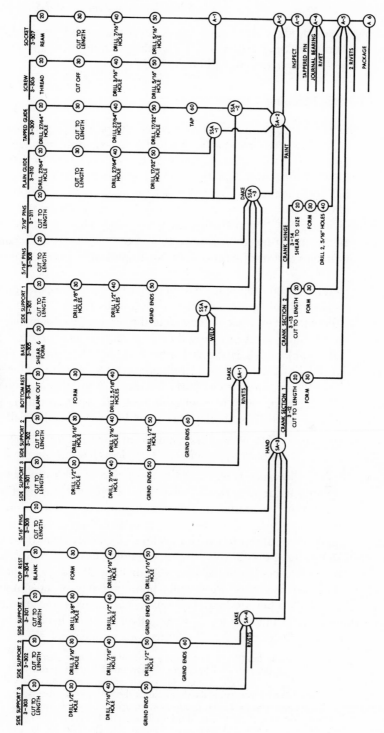

for piece part production can be adapted to paper work type production. Later when discussing arrangement planning techniques a special technique for office arrangement will be introduced.

The Layout Planning Chart

To this point in planning we have defined the product, operations necessary to produce required parts, the tentative assembly sequences, required inspections, and standard times. It is now necessary to determine the number of machines and the amount of direct labor necessary to accomplish these operations. In order to determine these quantities, however, additional data is necessary such as demand forecasts, operator performance levels, work period, process losses, and machine maintenance requirements. In order to organize this data with the corresponding necessary moves and in-process storage use is made of the layout planning chart.

In general, a layout planning chart is prepared for each operation sheet or route sheet. At this point, however, decisions as to level of operations must be known. For example, to complete the heading of the layout planning chart decisions must be reached on annual production requirements (pieces per year) which is derived after knowing the forecast product sales followed by decisions on overall production capacity.[5] Pieces per year provide the required piece parts for the forecast demand quantity plus an allowance for scrap or nonusable parts. If replacement parts are to be produced an additional allowance must be made. Symbolically:

$$\text{Pieces/year} = [(\text{Product sales requirement})(\text{assembly/product}) \\ (\text{pieces/assembly})] / (1 - \text{loss allowance})$$

where the loss allowance is expressed as a fraction of total product or, in terms of quality assurance, fraction defective. Note that the fraction defective is not that generated in the part manufacture alone, but must include an allowance for all succeeding operations during which the part in question may be subject to loss, for example, assembly operations losses. We will look more closely at this when determining machine requirements.

Days per year is operating days per year making allowance for holidays and vacations as necessary. Production hours per day is the number of clock hours worked per working day. Lot size is the expected quantity to be included in a production lot as it may affect material handling and in-process storage. Determination of optimal procurement lot sizes for raw

[5] Depending upon the long term objectives established by top management relating to the percentage of expected overall market and particular market segments, together with long term product planning and financing considerations, management will make decisions on overall production capacity. Sometimes these decisions specify excess capacity in terms of plant size and even production equipment for current sales requirements. See Timms, *op. cit.*, chap. 5, and William T. Morris, *The Capacity Decision System* (Irwin Series in Operations Management [Homewood, Ill.: Richard D. Irwin, Inc., 1967]).

materials, product components, and assemblies can be done only when process operations, equipment, and its layout are established. Accordingly, for planning the physical facilities a prior preliminary decision on expected lot sizes is required. Production control specialists will normally be expected to provide this input to the decision system for plant planning.[6] Procurement lot sizes are not to be confused, however, with in-plant materials movement lot sizes. Procurement lots may be combined but more frequently split to facilitate handling and reduced "thru-put time."

Moving now to the body of the chart note the provision for developing a flow chart. It will be observed, however, that no provision is made for charting delays as in the normal flow chart. The reason for this is that in plant layout analysis a delay generates a storage problem. In normal flow analysis storage and delay are differentiated by the time before the succeeding movement. In plant layout work if a delay exists storage must be provided, the amount of storage being dependent upon the accumulation of items between movements. Since either delay or storage in the process chart sense generates storage in the plant no differentiation is made for the layout planning chart.

Standard times for operations on the chart should be indicated as being measured in minutes or hours to avoid later confusion.[7] Other column headings prior to machine requirements are self-explanatory. Critical to the total layout planning process is the determination of machine requirements and although critical it is probably the most difficult in a real sense due to the necessity to incorporate a number of estimates and assumptions in its determination. This is further complicated by the fact that when machine quantities are established a static condition is generated which must then be adapted by production planning and scheduling to the dynamically changing product mix and demand which will exist in the future. Layout planning usually cannot assume a fixed production schedule but rather must attempt to provide sufficient production capacity in order that it can be adapted by planning and scheduling to those dynamic future demands. We now look at formulations by which the layout planner attempts to accomplish this sufficiency of capacity.

Determination of Machine Requirements[8] under the Assumption of Perfect Information

Before the production system, composed of all production and assembly equipment and the operating personnel, can be designed it is necessary to

6 For a full discussion of procurement lot size decisions, see James H. Greene, *Operations Planning and Control* (Irwin Series in Operations Management [Homewood, Ill.: Richard D. Irwin, Inc., 1967]), chap. 4.

7 The determination of standard times is treated in Nadler, *op. cit.*, chap. 9.

8 For a full treatment, see Ruddell Reed, Jr., *Plant Layout: Factors, Principles, and Techniques* (Homewood, Ill.: Richard D. Irwin, Inc., 1961), chaps. 6 and 7.

determine system components, in this case quantities of individual equipment and personnel types. Ideally the system designer should be able to work from system requirements and total criteria to component selection. We shall look later at a pseudo means of accomplishing this but first we will consider the traditional method of determining machine and manpower (component) requirements with the inherent assumption of perfect information.

We first look at determination of machine requirements (we will later show this is identical to the method of determination of manpower requirements). The principal factors upon which machine requirements for a particular operation depends are: (1) total number of production cycles, P, required of the operation, over some unit time interval; (2) the time required to perform the operation, T; (3) the length of the unit time interval, H, and (4) the use or utilization of the machine, C. The number of machines, N, required for an operation, is then:

$$N = \frac{TP}{HC}$$

Certain precautions must be taken in calculating N. First, since P is the total requirements it must include the total of the good item output of the operation plus an allowance for bad work which can be expected from the operation. Bad work is most frequently expressed as fraction defective and fraction defective is expressed as the fraction of the input which is found to be defective after completion of the operation.[9] Therefore:

$$P = \frac{GP}{1 - f}$$

where GP is the required good output and f is the fraction defective. For example, if $GP = 900$ and $f = 0.10$ then $P = \frac{GP}{1 - f} = \frac{900}{1 - 0.10} = 1000$. Note also the GP and P must be the quantity required for the time period, H. It does not matter in the formula what time is used for H so long as the same time period is used for all operations and the required P is for that period. Note, however, that time per operation, T, is normally expressed in hours or minutes and since, TP, is the total production requirement, H must also be expressed in the same units, hours or minutes. Since T in minutes can be converted to hours by dividing by 60 (minutes per hour) the convention is to express H in hours per unit time period (day, week, or year) after converting T to hours per operation. Time per operation, T, is normally available from the standards group as a standard time value. Hours per unit time period is normally thought of as clock hours. For the formula to hold both T and H must be in common units, either both in standard hours or both in clock hours. Clock hours for the operation is nothing but average time per operation. The transformation to a common

---
[9] Decision systems for determination of fraction defective are explained in Robert B. Fetter, *The Quality Control System* (Irwin Series in Operations Management [Homewood, Ill.: Richard D. Irwin, Inc., 1967]), chaps. 2 and 3.

time measurement is probably most easily accomplished by multiplying the clock hours per unit time period, equivalent to H, by the expected operator performance against standard. For example, if we expect to work 250 eight-hour days or 2000 clock hours per year but the performance against standard is expected to be 110 percent, then the number of standard hours per year will be 2000 × 1.10 or 2200 standard hours.

Use or utilization, C, is taken as the expected utilization of the machine under consideration assuming there are no delays for lack of work. The result then is:

$$\text{Number of machines for operation } p, N = \frac{T \text{ in standard hours} \times P \text{ in total units}/H \text{ hours}}{H \text{ in standard hours/unit time period} \times C}.$$

Note that since the standard time per operation may be for either crew or machine as can C, the same formula can be used for determining crew requirements for the operation by substituting the crew related T and C values. If a single operator is used the requirement calculated is manpower. Note, also, that since single levels of each input factor are used it is inherently assumed that these values are known explicitly or if average values are used provisioning is based upon expected value at steady state conditions. Means of evaluating the nature and effect of variation existing in the above formula input factors will be considered later. For the present, we will determine total machine requirements while continuing the assumption of perfect information.

Production required (P) will vary considerably between operations due primarily to two factors: each preceding operation must produce quantities which will become nonrecoverable bad work in succeeding operations and the quality level which can be maintained will vary with personnel, equipment, material, tolerances, method of operation, and method of control involved for each operation. The total production required is equal to the required good product plus bad work or expressed symbolically, $P = (P_G + P_{BW})$, where P_G represents required good product and P_{BW} represents nonrecoverable bad work. Time and capacity is spent on bad work as well as good work. The problem is to determine the good product requirements and the expected bad work for each operation.

The good product for the final operation (O_n) is equal to the expected sales requirements. The good products requirements for the next-to-last operation (O_{n-1}) is equal to the good product for O_n plus the expected nonrecoverable bad work generated by O_n. (Nonrecoverable bad work is most often scrap, rejects, seconds, or other lower quality, reworkable for sale. Products may be nonrecoverable as good product although not to be discarded as scrap.) $P_{G(O_{n-1})}$ then is equal to $P_{G(O_n)} + P_{BW(O_n)}$ and $P_{G(O_{n-2})} = P_{G(O_{n-1})} + P_{BW(O_{n-1})}$, and so forth. If $P_{G(O_n)}$ is established, P for each preceding operation can be estimated if P_{BW} for that operation and all succeeding operations is determined.

In addition to nonrecoverable bad work, there is often additional bad work which by rework can be recovered as good quality product. This portion of bad work does not affect the determination of preceding operation good product requirements, but it does affect the total production required of each operation. Time must be spent to rework these items and additional equipment must be provided. The time required for rework may be greater than the time required to perform the operation originally due to each rework piece having its own peculiar requirements. This requires additional analysis by the operator as well as quality control or process engineers who may specify the rework. Due to these individually peculiar requirements separate rework areas or departments may be established or the rework may be scheduled during idle machine periods. The choice depends primarily upon cost and control factors. Under either choice equipment excessive to first run requirements may be determined separately using times applicable to the rework operation. To differentiate the rework load, it should be determined using the formula:

$$N' = \frac{T'P'}{HC}$$

where N' = number of machines required for rework, T' = time assigned for rework, and P' = number of pieces submitted for rework. In the basic machine requirement determination this amount will be distributed between P_G and P_{BW} in that after rework a portion will become usable and the remainder will become scrap.

If the decision is to perform rework operations within the production areas, N' should be added to N to determine total machine requirements for the operation. If a separate rework area is to be used, N' is the requirement of that area.

To properly estimate values of P_{BW} and P', historical data is necessary. Historical data should be analyzed to determine probable effects of variations between the conditions under which it was gathered and the conditions under the new layout. If control limits can be established and an analysis made of reject causes, an attempt can be made to eliminate or reduce the major sources of the causes for rejects under the new process.

When historical data is not available, an analysis of the combined effects of interacting factors likely to produce rejects should be made. A partial list of factors determining reject levels is:

1. Equipment.
2. Materials.
3. Tools and forming methods.
4. Maintenance policies.
5. Product design and specifications.
6. Quality assurance and effectiveness.
7. Personnel.

Space does not permit full considerations and analysis of each of these factors.

Use Factor

The use factor, or the ratio of probable maximum equipment availability to total production hours, is primarily dependent upon the nature or design of the equipment being considered, continuity of equipment use, and maintenance policy.

As the complexity of equipment design increases the potential causes of equipment malfunctioning increases. This results in a lowered use factor. The quality and quantity of the product will most likely be increased by incorporating higher degrees of specialization and control in the equipment, but the mechanisms incorporated and controls normally become more complex in individual design and interrelationships. It is therefore necessary to increase the reliability of individual components if high reliability of the equipment system is to be realized. Most often, the increased reliability of components can only be realized by improved preventive maintenance programs.

Maintenance policy and practices will have a greater effect on the use factor than either the nature of the equipment or the continuity of equipment use. It is highly unlikely that a maximum use factor can be expected without a well-planned, organized, and administered preventive maintenance program. Such a program will anticipate need for repair and avoid a number of breakdowns and slowdowns of equipment. If the program includes persons to develop methods for maintenance operations and to develop statistically optimal maintenance schedules, the use factor may be increased considerably.

Total Requirements of a Machine Type

When determining the number of machines required per operation, the calculated requirement will be either a fraction or a mixed number. If only the one operation is to be performed on an individual machine each of the calculated requirements would be raised to the next highest whole number. The result of such a procedure would be to provide the maximum total machine requirement with inherent high idle time. The minimum requirement for an individual machine type would be the next higher whole number above the sum of all fractional and mixed number requirements for individual operations performed on that machine. At least in theory, there should be some manner by which this minimum number of machines could be scheduled to provide the required yearly production. If this is attempted, however, we often find an excessive number of setups required or scheduled idle periods which in many cases makes the use of this minimal requirement impractical. Therefore, the desired number of machines for a particular type will lie between the minimum and the maximum.

FIGURE 4–9

LAYOUT PLANNING CHART

PART NO. 3-300 PART NAME LIGHT DUTY JACK PCS./ASSY. 35 ASSY. REQ./YR 18,000 SHEET ___ OF ___

ASSY. NO. 1 ASSY. NAME A-5 ASSY./PRODUCT 12 PRODUCTION HRS./DAY 6.4 STD. HRS. PREPARED BY ___ DATE ___

MATERIAL STEEL SIZE — PCS./DAY 2540 LOT SIZE ___ APPROVED BY ___ DATE ___

ST. NO.	F M S I	DESCRIPTION	OPER. NO.	DEPT. NO.	STD. MIN. OR HRS.	MACHINE OR EQUIPMENT	MACHINES REQD			OPER. PER MACH.	TOTAL MANPOWER				HANDLING REQUIREMENTS				REMARKS
							MACH. FRAC.	COMB. WITH	MACH. REQD.		CREW FRAC.	MAN. FRAC.	COMB. WITH	MEN REQD.	HOW MOVED	CONT. TYPE	LOAD SIZE	DIST. MOVED	
	●	RIVET SIDE SUPPORT 2 & 3 FOR SA-1	1		.00182	HAND PRESS DAKE 1 TON	.0258	—	1	1	.0258	.0258	3-0-20 3-0-50 3-0-90	1					
	●	RIVET SIDE SUPPORT 2 & 3 FOR SA-4	2		.00182	SAME AS ABOVE	.0258	—	—	1	.0258	.0258	3-0-10 3-0-50 3-0-90	—					
	➤	MOVE TO ASSEMBLY STATION #4																	
	●	PIN SIDE SUPPORTS TO TOP. REST (SA-3)	3		.00652		.0784			1	.0784	.0784							
	●	WELD BOTTOM REST TO BASE (SSA-4)	4		.00185	ARC WELDER LINCOLN 440A	.0192	—	1	1	.0192	.0192	—	1					
	➤	MOVE TO ASSEMBLY STATION #4																	
	●	PIN SIDE SUPPORTS TO BOTTOM REST (SSA-3)	5		.00560	HAND PRESS DAKE 1 TON	.0795	—	—	1	.0795	.0795	3-0-10 3-0-20 3-0-90	—					
	➤	MOVE TO ASSEMBLY STATION #4																	
	●	INSERT PINS INTO TAPPED SCREW GUIDES	6		.00127					1	.0180	.0180							
	●	INSERT PINS INTO PLAIN SCREW GUIDE	7		.00127					1	.0180	.0180							
	➤	MOVE TO ASSEMBLY STATION #4																	
	●	INSERT SOCKET ON SCREW	8		.00047					1	.0067	.0067							
	➤	MOVE TO ASSEMBLY STATION #5																	
	●	ASSEMBLE SA-3 & SSA-3 WITH GUIDES & PAINT	9		.67000	HAND PRESS DAKE 1 TON	.0258	—	—	1	9.500	9.500	3-0-10 3-0-20 3-0-50	—					
	➤	MOVE TO ASSEMBLY STATION #5																	
	●	INSERT SCREW, BEARING, RIVET & PIN	10		.00845					1	.1200	.1200							
	●	ASSEMBLE CRANK AREA	11		.00278					1	.0394	.0394							
	➤	MOVE TO PACKAGING AREA																	

In a process arrangement (equipment grouped by type not product produced), it is recognized that the supervisor or area planner must be responsible to load equipment in such a manner as to meet the required schedule by assigning work in the most economical manner within schedule limits. The question of economics normally results in assigning machines in such a manner that setups approach a minimum, thereby resulting in greater productive time on the equipment. Furthermore, in times of abnormal load requirements overtime, with its increased unit cost, may be used to overcome production backlogs. For layout planning it is not necessary, nor wise, to develop detailed production schedules. Conditions will change and the most the layout can hope to provide are facilities capable of handling these dynamic variations. Necessary facilities for objective production estimates, assuming good scheduling by production control, may be provided by layout assigning to each machine a combination of operations collectively requiring no more than 100 percent of the available machine time under normal conditions. This is accomplished by summing fractional machine requirements for individual operations until total requirements on individual machines approach unity. When summed operation fractional requirements indicate a mixed number of machines, the mixed number can be reduced to N units plus a fraction. The fractional portion of the mixed number can then be handled in the same manner as a fractional operation requirement and the units portion assumed to represent machines fully utilized at unity requirement. To illustrate, let us assume the following requirements for a particular model of automatic lathe:

Requirement Number	Operation Number	Fractional Machine Requirements	Combined with	Total Machine Requirements
1 3718-10		1.78	7674-70	2
2 7674-70		4.08	3718-10	4
3 1894-40		2.51	4671-30	3
4 4671-90		2.21	......	2
5 1867-30		3.37	1894-40	4
Total		13.95		15

For the first requirement we must provide the next higher whole number of machines or two. However, when we do, we have 0.22 machine excess assignments. This can be used to satisfy the fractional requirement of requirement number 2 or requirement number 4. Number 4, however, can also be assigned with numbers 3 or 5 without exceeding unity. By assigning number 2 with number 1 and number 3 with number 4, the total fraction requirement on any assignment is a minimum with the minimum reasonable number of operations assigned to an individual machine. Requirement number 5 is not combined and the total requirement is 15 by this assignment. The total of the fractional machine requirements is 13.95.

The total machine requirements after combination exceed the minimum possible obtained by adding fractional requirements, e.g., 14. It will be possible to overcome this by dividing portions of a fractional requirement (e.g., 0.37 of operation 5) over several machines. Remember, however, that increased assignments mean increased setups resulting in a lower use factor. Therefore, there will be a practical limit as to the variety of jobs to be assigned an individual machine, or to the variety of machines to which an individual operation may be assigned.

Manpower Balance

When one man operates one machine manpower is balanced in the same manner as are machines attempting to have all men of like skills assigned duties which as nearly as possible have the same total requirement.

When crews are used on certain operations the method of handling the balance differs slightly. When a crew is used on an operation the entire crew may be assigned to another operation requiring the same crew size during available time, or individual crew members may be assigned individually during the free time. In either case, it must be determined that it is not necessary for the combined assignments of a single operator to be performed simultaneously.

After eliminating simultaneous operations the following steps may be followed in balancing:

1. Combine jobs where possible that require the same crew size. This is identical to the procedure in balancing machines.
2. If combination with equal crew sizes is not possible, assume the next higher whole number crew requirement and locate operations in the chart requiring smaller crews or individual operator jobs each of which has additional fractional requirements approaching that available from the crew being considered. Select smaller crews and individuals with approximately equal fractional requirements such that individuals plus sum of smaller crew sizes equals size of crew being combined. Distribute the excess manpower of the larger crew among the individual jobs and smaller crews to obtain the balance, being certain no interference between jobs assigned to an individual is created.

REVIEW QUESTIONS

1. Discuss the production facilities relationship to total plant facilities.
2. Comment on Figure 4–1.
3. What is the primary objective of any facility? How is this objective satisfied?
4. Discuss Figure 4–2.
5. What is the basic input data for initial facility planning and where do we obtain this data?

6. Explain the purpose of each of the following in facilities planning:
   a) Product drawings.
   b) Assembly sheets.
   c) Operation sheets.
   d) Layout planning charts.
7. How do demand forecasts affect layout planning?
8. Explain the significance of each factor in the formula for determining machine requirements for an operation under the assumption of perfect information.
9. Explain why manpower requirements must initially be determined on the basis of crew requirements rather than man requirements.
10. Explain how total requirements of a machine type or model are determined explaining the significance of any assumptions incorporated in the procedure.

PROBLEMS

1. Given an operation with a standard time of .08 hours per part. Similar operations are being accomplished at 80 percent of standard on the average. How many work stations for the operation will be required if the sales forecast is for 25,000 units to be produced during 242 eight-hour shifts if equipment use is limited to about .85 and .02 bad work is expected?

2. What is the total manpower requirements for the following set of operations?

Operation Number	Crew Size	Standard Time in Hours	Required Production	Fraction Defection
1	4	.07	20,000	.01
2	2	.05	12,000	.005
3	1	.04	10,000	.02

The plant works 250 eight-hour shifts per year, plant performance is .90 of standard, and both equipment and manpower use may be .85.

Chapter 5

A PROBABILISTIC MODEL FOR DETERMINING MACHINE REQUIREMENTS

IN CHAPTER 4 machine requirements for a single operation was established by the formula:

$$N = \frac{TP}{HC} \qquad\qquad \text{Eq. 5-1}$$

Inherent in any formula requiring a single input value for each variable are the assumptions of decision under certainty and either static conditions or insignificant variation of inputs. In production activities these assumptions may prove to be critical. We can remove the conditions of certainty and static inputs if we can define the distributional nature of input variables and their joint actions on the objective requirement, in this case number of machines required for an operation, N.

Without any loss of generality we can write the above as:

$$N = f(T, P, H, C)$$

which merely states that the number of machines is a function of time per piece, production quantity required, the time available to provide production requirements, and the utilization level for the equipment or machine. To go further requires explicit definition of the variables. It is doubtful that any set of distributions of individual variables applies for all cases encountered. However, definition of the nature and action of the input variables under common conditions will provide not only a feasible probabilistic model for machine requirements but a useful model to evaluate the effect of variable inputs. We therefore look at each input variable separately and then jointly.

H, Hours per Unit Time Period

If *H* is expressed as standard hours per time period then it is equivalent to the actual hours per time period, H_a, measured in clock units, multiplied by *A*, the performance against standard measured as the decimal equivalent of the ratio of standard hours earned to actual hours worked. Furthermore, actual hours per period (for example, day) can be considered constant since it is established by management decree and *T*, the standard time per operation, is also a constant established by normal work measurement systems. Therefore, by substitution:

$$N = \frac{TP}{HC}$$
$$= \frac{T}{H_a A} \cdot \frac{P}{C} \qquad \text{Eq. 5–2}$$

Note that so long as the same unit time period is used to measure H_a and *P*, the length of the period does not affect the model.

Use of Average Actual Time per Operation, $\bar{t}_a$, Rather Than *T*

By the central limit theorem, the distribution of the average actual time per operation, $\bar{t}_a$, will be approximately normal. Furthermore:

$$A = \frac{T}{\bar{t}_a} \qquad \text{Eq. 5–3}$$

where *T* is the standard time per operation. Substituting in Eq. 5–2:

$$N = \frac{T}{H_a A} \cdot \frac{P}{C}$$
$$= \frac{T \bar{t}_a}{H_a T} \cdot \frac{P}{C}$$
$$= \frac{\bar{t}_a}{H_a} \cdot \frac{P}{C} \qquad \text{Eq. 5–4}$$

Independence of Average Actual Time

At this point the question as to the independence of $\bar{t}_a$ arises. There is little question that over the short run, production demand on a shop, department, or operator affects performance and average actual time. However, if load trend continues upward or downward management adjusts the labor force upward or downward. The specific time at which these reduced loads occur are not in general predictable, being dependent upon immediate general economic, sales, and production conditions. But so long as management policy and practice remains constant and standards continue to be established in the same manner as in the past, we can reasonably expect the frequency distribution of average actual time for next year, or following years, to be similar to that of the past. By this argument it is assumed that the distribution of average actual time is independent of annual production requirements. (This in turn results in the necessity for using as the time period of the model a production year.)

Furthermore, since we are not primarily concerned with parameters of the distribution of individual cycle times, it is not necessary that the individual sample in terms of number of cycles timed be constant. Letting $\bar{t}_a$ be the random variable:

$$\mu_{\bar{t}_a} = \frac{\displaystyle\sum_{i=1}^{N} t_i}{\displaystyle\sum_{i=1}^{N} n_i} = \mu_{t_a} \qquad \text{Eq. 5-5}$$

in which:

$\mu_{\bar{t}_a}$ is an estimate of the mean of the distribution of $\bar{t}_a$
t_i is the total actual time of the i-th sample
n_i is the number of operation cycles in the i-th sample
N is the number of samples
μ_{t_a} is an estimate of the mean of the distribution of t_a

and the variance of $\bar{t}_a$ is estimated by $s_{\bar{t}_a}^2$.

$$s_{\bar{t}_a}^2 = \frac{\displaystyle\sum_{i=1}^{N} (\bar{t}_{a_i} - \mu_{\bar{t}_a})^2}{N - 1} \qquad \text{Eq. 5-6}$$

The permissive use of variable sample size may be of value in practice since a convenient sample size is the production per time period or units per lot. Neither of these are constants.

DETERMINATION OF TOTAL PRODUCTION

Requirements, P for an Operation

The determination of total production requirements for an operation is dependent upon two major factors: the total sales requirements for the part or product for whose production the operation is required; and the expected losses of quantity resulting from the operation under consideration, and all preceding and succeeding operations required to complete the part or product. If sales and losses could be predicted with certainty the problem would be trivial. However, uncertainty exists and some risk must be assumed due to forecast errors.

In long-range sales forecasting two basic methods are normally used: a single forecast quantity is determined by a forecasting model, or a forecast is obtained after considering a number of independent estimates.

If estimates of sales are made by the second method the final forecast is in fact made by the principle of expectation, from decision theory:

$$E(sa) = \sum_{i=1}^{n} P_i(sa_i) \qquad \text{Eq. 5–7}$$

where:

$E(sa)$ is the resultant expected sales quantity for product

(sa_i) is the predicted sales quantity by estimate i

P_i is the probability of (sa_i), $\sum_{i=1}^{N} P_i = 1$

n is the number of individual estimates, or sample size.

If $P_1 = P_2 = \ldots = P_n$, $E(sa)$ is the arithmetic average of the individual estimates. If all P_i's are not equal $E(sa)$ is a weighted average. The method of assigning P_i's does not enter into the model. For the first case $E(sa)$ is the direct estimate.

The Estimate of Total Production Requirements for an Operation with $E(sa)$ Known for Product

By any inspection operation for a single item, only three primary decisions are available. A part is good, bad, or reworkable. If reworkable then after rework it is reinspected and the decision process continued until the decision reduces to good or bad. This permits the consideration of each item inspected as being drawn from a universe having a fraction defective p'. We can represent the distribution of defectives by the binomial distribution which can be approximated by the normal distribution whose mean and standard deviation are the same as those for the binomial.

The production process for a product is a series of individual operations performed in some assigned sequence. Each of these operations may produce defectives which are removed before the next operation commences.

If we now assume that all defectives found are removed immediately prior to the operation of interest, the number of items expected to be passed through the operation of interest will be the quantity started through the process minus the expected cumulative defectives removed by inspection. Symbolically:

$$E(n) = Q - P_{p'}Q \qquad \text{Eq. 5–8}$$

where:

$E(n)$ is the expected value of n, the number of items passed through the operation of interest per year

Q is the quantity started through the process per year

$P_{p'}$ is the fraction defective generated per year by all operations prior to the operation of interest.

One further assumption is now made. If $E(np') \leqq 5$ or if fewer than 100 good units of a product are required per year, it is assumed that this product will be grouped with other low quantity items to establish a product class. This product class will then be used for facility planning purposes rather than the individual products.

Since it has been assumed earlier that $E(sa)$ will be used as the value of required sales, this must be equal to quantity of good units or $E(n_g)$ for the final operation or finished product. For any operation other than the last $E(n_g)$ will be equal to $u_j E(sa)^1$ (where u_j is the number of part j's in the finished product), plus the expected cumulative defectives for all operations following the operation of interest. Symbolically:

$$E(n_g)_i = u_j E(sa) + \sum_{i=1}^{n} E(n)_i p'_i \qquad \text{Eq. 5-9}$$

Furthermore, $Q(1 - p_p) = n_i$ and therefore n_i is distributed approximately normal with

$$\widehat{\mu}_{n_i} = Q(1 - \widehat{p}_p) = E(\widehat{n}_i) \qquad \text{Eq. 5-10}$$

and:

$$\widehat{\sigma}_{n_i}{}^2 = Q\widehat{p}_p(1 - \widehat{p}_p) \qquad \text{Eq. 5-11}$$

n_i, the number of items passing through the operation of interest, is equal to P, the operation cycles per time period, for that operation and therefore the distribution of n_i represents the distribution of P, the total production requirements, or operation cycles per time period.

Determination of the Distribution of the Use Factor

There is a tendency to confuse the use factor with a utilization factor. The use factor tends to be the upper limit of the utilization factor. The utilization factor is defined as the ratio of hours of equipment use to total hours available over some unit time period, frequently one production year. Utilization is therefore dependent upon the load or demand requirement against the machine, as well as the ability of the machine to perform without malfunction or stoppage for preventive maintenance. If load requirements were sufficient to place a demand on the machine at all times when it was available the utilization factor would approach a maximum ≤ 1. At this maximum level the ratio for utilization would be rewritten as the ratio of hours of equipment use to the sum of hours of equipment use plus hours lost for maintenance, since the denominator in the maximum

---

[1] It can be shown that if $E(n_g)$ is known and p' estimated by the best possible means the maximum deviation we can expect in n from $E(n)$ with 95 percent confidence is approximately $0.0755\ E(n)$, if $E(n_g) \geqq 100$ and $p' \leqq 0.5$. As $E(n_g) \gg 100$ and if p' deviates from 0.35 the maximum expected deviation is reduced. The more likely values to be encountered in practice are $E(n_g) \gg 100$ and $p' \ll 0.35$, and therefore, it is reasonable to expect the deviation to be much less than $0.0755\ E(n)$.

case would be equal to total production hours available over the unit time period. We can write this ratio as:

$$\text{Max}\left\{\frac{\text{hours of equipment use}}{\text{hours lost to maintenance} + \text{hours of equipment use}}\right\} = C, \text{the use factor,}$$

and C is a continuous random variable having limits 0 to 1.

If we invert the ratio, and designate it U, it remains a random variable but with limits 1 to ∞. If we substitute U for $\frac{1}{C}$ in the previous equation, we can write the model as:

$$H = \frac{1}{H_a} \cdot f(\bar{t}_a, P, U) \qquad \text{Eq. 5–12}$$

Since it is desirable to maximize C when its inverse U is the variable of interest it is desirable to seek minimization of U. Under ideal conditions $U = 1.0$. Since ideal conditions are virtually never realized in practice $U > 1.0$, but the objective of management is to have $U \longrightarrow 1.0$, within the bounds of optimizing economies.

As defined above, U is largely dependent upon reliability characteristics of the equipment, replacement policy of the firm, and maintenance practices. Closely related are the factors of setup time and scheduling inefficiencies. These last two, however, result primarily due to multiorder or multiproduct effects and will be considered later when analyzing the combination of individual operation requirements to determine total machine model requirements.

Reliability is defined as the probability that a device will perform, without failure, a specified function under given conditions for a specified period of time. Three types of failure are normally considered: (1) wearout failure, a progressive reduction of capability until failure; (2) chance failure, those failures which are unpredictable and equally likely to occur at any time in life; and (3) initial failure or infant mortality, the failures due to "newness" which normally are corrected during run-in. Initial failures will not be considered as affecting operating conditions since they are eliminated during "shakedown," or running in before placing the equipment on-line for normal production.

Reliability is concerned with the frequency of system stoppage or malfunction. Actual repair time for a malfunction maintenance operation will vary in the same manner as discussed for a production operation time and as a result can be approximated by a normal distribution. Actual times for periodically scheduled preventive maintenance will also be distributed approximately as a normal distribution in the same manner as for malfunction repair times. Periodically scheduled preventive maintenance operations are normally scheduled to be performed after the passage of a fixed period of time following the previous maintenance operation occurrence, frequently expressed in number of working hours or working days, degree of use during this period not being considered. If this schedule is maintained deviation of time between identical maintenance operations on a machine is inconsequential and as a result maintenance time per unit time period is distributed as the sum of actual times for individual occurrences which is the sum of a series of normal distributions. In practice, however, an assignment of operations is made to a preventive maintenance man or crew on a fixed sequence basis, the total period assigned to the cycle being equal to the sum of average time for each operation. From the above, it is known that individual operation actual times are random variables normally distributed about the average and therefore the time between occurrences of the operation assigned to a fixed position in the cycles must be the sum of a number of independent normally distributed random variables. But the sum of a number of independent normally distributed random variables is also normally distributed and therefore time between occurrences of a periodically scheduled maintenance operation must also be normally distributed. The preventive maintenance time per unit time period for a single operation must equal the product of number of occurrences and time per occurrence. But both of these factors are normally distributed random variables and independent in the statistical sense. The product of two independent normally distributed random variables is approximately normally distributed.

For chance failures Lloyd and Lipow state as a general rule that the estimate of the reliability function, R, defined as the probability of success, "is approximately normally distributed when n, the sample size, is large."[2] But $R = 1 - F$ where F is the failure time distribution function, and as R is normally distributed. Again, time per unit time period for chance failure maintenance must equal the product of the number of occurrences and time per occurrence and since each is an independent normally distributed random variable, the product is approximately normally distributed.

Preventive maintenance which is based upon the number of recurring production cycles since the previous maintenance is dependent upon demand. If we assume demand constant, time between occurrences is assumed to be normally distributed with mean equal to the product of the number of production cycles and the mean time per production cycle, and variance equal to the product of the number of production cycles and the variance of the individual production cycle time (by the additivity rule for variances). If, on the other hand, demand is approximately normally distributed as indicated earlier, the distribution of time between maintenance operations will also be approximately normal since it is the product of two independent normal variables, demand and time per operation cycles.

If time required per unit time period for each of the three types of

---

[2] D. K. Lloyd and M. Lipow, *Reliability: Management, Methods, and Mathematics* (Englewood Cliffs, N.J., Prentice-Hall, Inc., 1962).

maintenance—periodically scheduled preventive, cyclic scheduled preventive, and chance occurrence—is considered independent and if each can be approximated by a normal distribution, then the total time for maintenance per unit time period can be approximated by a normal distribution. The total time for maintenance per unit time period is the time lost for maintenance in our expression for U.

Hours of equipment use is going to be a random variable resulting from the additive influences of a number of independent and dependent variables including those associated with equipment reliability, firm maintenance policies, and replacement policies as well as demand for production and average time per production operation. An extension of the central limit theorem says that "if x is the sum of a number of independent variables $y_1, y_2, \ldots, y_n$, then whatever the distributions of the individual y's (subject to very general restrictions), the distribution of x approaches the normal form as the number of variables n gets larger and larger."[3] Feller states, "the central limit theorem holds also for large classes of dependent variables."[4] By this extension we can expect the hours of equipment use to be distributed approximately normally, particularly if the period production demand remains reasonably stable over the measured time interval which is inherent in our earlier assumption of $E(sa)$ as annual demand.

Now let H_m be the hours lost to maintenance and let H_u be the hours of equipment use. Then:

$$U = \frac{H_m + H_u}{H_u} = \frac{H_m}{H_u} + 1 \qquad \text{Eq. 5-13}$$

But H_m, except for time required for that preventive maintenance scheduled on the basis of fixed time intervals, will have a dependency relationship with H_u, related to operating cycles or chance associated with equipment operation. This dependency may be approximated by a linear regression equation, $H_m = c + mH_u$, where c is the constant or intercept value of H_m and m is the slope of the regression line, representing the rate of change in H_m as H_u increases. Substituting this into Eq. 5-13:

$$U = m + 1 + c \left[\frac{1}{H_u} \right] \qquad \text{Eq. 5-14}$$

(Since H_m and H_u are each normal, the regression of H_m on H_u is linear, and the conditional variance of H_m is independent of the value assumed by H_u.)

The following procedure may be used to obtain an estimate of the distribution of U. First, group operations which can be considered to have equal U due to similarity of material and/or operation complexity, and operator skills.

[3] C. D. Flagle, W. H. Huggins, and R. H. Roy, *Operations Research and Systems Engineering* (Baltimore: The Johns Hopkins Press, 1960).

[4] W. Feller, *An Introduction to Probability Theory and Its Application,* 2d ed. (New York: John Wiley & Sons, Inc., 1957).

Now, $\bar{t}_a P$ is an estimate of the number of operating hours required for an operation or equipment use hours, H_u. By our earlier assumption of linear regression approximation of hours lost to maintenance from hours of equipment use, U is dependent upon $\bar{t}_a P$, the estimate of H_u. We therefore use $\bar{t}_a P$ as an estimate of the relative weight of each U_z as it affects the machine model U. Letting $\widehat{U}$ be the estimate of U, for each machine model:

$$\widehat{U} = \sum_{z=1}^{k} \frac{\bar{t}_{a_z} P_z U_z}{\displaystyle\sum_{z=1}^{k} \bar{t}_{a_z} P_z} \qquad\qquad \text{Eq. 5-15}$$

where k is the total number of groups the operations on the machine model are subdivided into, z is the group, and:

$$\bar{t}_{a_z} P_z = \sum_{j=1}^{h_z} \bar{t}_{a_j} P_j = h_z \overline{(\bar{t}_{a_j} P_j)} \qquad\qquad \text{Eq. 5-16}$$

where:

$j =$ the individual operation within group z

$h_z =$ the number of operations within group z

$\overline{(\bar{t}_{a_j} P_j)} =$ the average value of $\bar{t}_{a_j} P_j$ for the group z.

The groups must be mutually exclusive by the method of establishment and by the usual work measurement assumption of basic motion elements being independent of preceding or succeeding operations, independent in the statistical sense.

It can be proved that if the distribution of individual random variables is normal and each random variable has a small coefficient of variation the product will be approximately normally distributed. Therefore, $f(\bar{t}_{a_j} P_j)$ is assumed normal.

The Distribution of Average Actual Time and Production Quantity

The problem of defining the distribution of $\displaystyle\sum_{j=1}^{n} \bar{t}_{a_j} P_j$, is the problem of defining the distribution of n independent normal variates. Now, as n random variables are each distributed normally, the distribution of their sum will also be normal. Furthermore, $\displaystyle\sum_{j=1}^{h} \bar{t}_{a_j} P_j = \bar{t}_{a_z} P_z$ and $\displaystyle\sum_{j=1}^{n} \bar{t}_{a_j} P_j$ can be considered approximately normally distributed.

The Joint Distribution with U

If U is equal for all the operations within any group performed on a machine:

$$U_z \doteq \frac{\sum\limits_{j=1}^{h_z} H_{mj} + \sum\limits_{j=1}^{h_z} H_{uj}}{\sum\limits_{j=1}^{h} H_{uj}}$$

where $U_z = U$ for the z-th group and h_z is the number of operations contained in the z-th group. Therefore:

$$E(U_1) \doteq E(U_2) \doteq \ldots \doteq E(U_h) \doteq E(U_j) \doteq E(U_z)$$

and:

$$E(U_z) = \left(\sum\limits_{j=1}^{h_z} H_{mj} + \sum\limits_{j=1}^{h_z} H_{uj} \right) \div \sum\limits_{j=1}^{h_z} H_{uj} \qquad \text{Eq. 5–17}$$

and:

$$\text{Var}U_z = \sum\limits_{j=1}^{h_z} \text{Var}U_j \left(\frac{E(\bar{t}_{a_j}P_j)}{\sum\limits_{j=1}^{h_z} E(\bar{t}_{a_j}P_j)} \right)^2 \qquad \text{Eq. 5–18}$$

since operations are assumed independent and the constants of multiplication between variances of independent random variables, U_j's, are

$\left(E(\bar{t}_{a_j}P_j) / \sum\limits_{j=1}^{h_z} E(\bar{t}_{a_j}P_j) \right)$, the relative frequency of individual operation

occurrence.

It can be shown that:

$$E(U) = \sum\limits_{z=1}^{k} \left(\frac{E(\bar{t}_{a_z}P_z)}{\sum\limits_{z=1}^{k} E(\bar{t}_{a_z}P_z)} \right) E(U_z)$$

and:

$$\text{Var}(U) \doteq \sum\limits_{z=1}^{k} \left(\frac{E(\bar{t}_{a_z}P_z)}{\sum\limits_{z=1}^{k} E(\bar{t}_{a_z}P_z)} \right)^2 \text{Var}(U_z)$$

Now substituting the expression for $\text{Var}(U_z)$:

$$\text{Var}(U) \doteq \sum\limits_{z=1}^{k} \left(\frac{E(\bar{t}_{a_z}P_z)}{\sum\limits_{z=1}^{k} E(\bar{t}_{a_z}P_z)} \right)^2 \sum\limits_{j=1}^{h_z} \left(\frac{E(\bar{t}_{a_j}P_j)}{\sum\limits_{j=1}^{h_z} E(\bar{t}_{a_j}P_j)} \right)^2 \text{Var}(U_j) \qquad \text{Eq. 5–19}$$

We now consider the effect of setup time on H_m. Setup time occurs whenever it is necessary to change a machine over from production of one operation to production of another. If a single machine produces an operation for all items in a production lot then the number of setups per year $= P/Q$, where Q is the size of the production lot. Standard times can be established for setups and therefore a $\bar{t}_a$ can be established for the setup operation. As a result, in this simplest case:

$$T_{sj} = \frac{P_j}{Q_j}\,\bar{t}_{sj} = \frac{1}{Q_j}P_j\bar{t}_{sj} \qquad \text{Eq. 5–20}$$

Where $T_{sj} =$ total annual setup time and Q_j is the lot size at operation j. $\bar{t}_{sj}$ is average setup time for operation j. Since $1/Q_j$ is assumed constant, T_{sj} is distributed approximately normally since $P_j\bar{t}_s$ has an approximately normal distribution.

If an expected value for the number of machines, $E(N_j)$, assigned to a specific operation could be determined, then:

$$T_{sj} = \frac{E(N_j)}{Q_j}P_j\bar{t}_{sj} \qquad \text{Eq. 5–21}$$

Let us assume that $E(N_j) = N$ by the method of Chapter 4, and therefore T_{sj}, a random variable, is distributed normally with mean and variance as follows:

$$E(T_{sj}) \doteq \frac{E(N_j)}{Q_j}E(\bar{t}_{sj}P_j) \qquad \text{Eq. 5–22}$$

$$\text{Var}(T_{sj}) \doteq \left(\frac{E(N_j)^2}{Q_j}\right)\sigma^2 P_j\bar{t}_{sj} \qquad \text{Eq. 5–23}$$

We can now write U_T for U including setup time and:

$$U_T = \frac{H_m + \displaystyle\sum_{j=1}^{n} T_{sj} + \displaystyle\sum_{z=1}^{k} \bar{t}_{a_z}P_z}{\displaystyle\sum_{z=1}^{k} \bar{t}_{a_z}P_z} \qquad \text{Eq. 5–24}$$

Each term in the expression for U_T has been shown to be a random variable, normally distributed for each operation j. Therefore, since each summation is a summation of normally distributed random variables each summation will also be normally distributed. However, $E(N_j)/Q_j$ is constant for operation j, and by linear combination for independent j's:

$$E\left(\sum_{j=1}^{n} T_{sj}\right) = \sum_{j=1}^{n} \frac{E(N_j)}{Q_j}E(P_j\bar{t}_{sj}) \qquad \text{Eq. 5–25}$$

and:

$$\text{Var}\left(\sum_{j=1}^{n} T_{sj}\right) \doteq \sum_{j=1}^{n}\left\{\left(\frac{E(N_j)}{Q_j}\right)^2 \text{Var}(P_j\bar{t}_{sj})\right\}. \qquad \text{Eq. 5–26}$$

$$\sigma_c^2 = \sum_{i=1}^{v} \left(\frac{H_a}{\Delta H_{t_{m_i}}} \right)^2 \sigma_{t_{m_i}}^2 \qquad \text{Eq. 5-27}$$

where c is the intercept of H_m on H_u, v is the total number of time interval scheduled preventive maintenance operations on the machine per unit time period, H_a is the total hours per unit time period, and $\Delta H_{t_{m_i}}$ is the hours between individual occurrences of operation i by schedule.

$$E(c) = \sum_{i=1}^{v} \frac{H_a}{\Delta H_{t_{m_i}}} E(\bar{t}_{m_i}) \qquad \text{Eq. 5-28}$$

Substituting in Eq. 5-24 gives:

$$U_T = (m+1) + \frac{\sum\limits_{j=1}^{n} (T_{s_j}) + c}{\sum\limits_{j=1}^{n} (\bar{t}_{a_j} P_j)} \qquad \text{Eq. 5-29}$$

Now $\left(\sum\limits_{j=1}^{n} T_{s_j} + c \right)$ is normally distributed since it is the sum of two normal random variables and it has been shown previous that $\sum\limits_{j=1}^{n} (\bar{t}_{a_j} P_j)$ is distributed normally, and the distribution of the ratio of the two normal variables will be approximately normally distributed.

The expression for the expected value and variance of U_T becomes:

$$E(U_T) = E(m) + 1 + \frac{\sum\limits_{j=1}^{n} \left[E(T_{s_j}) \right] + E(c)}{\sum\limits_{j=1}^{n} \left[E(\bar{t}_{a_j} P_j) \right]} \qquad \text{Eq. 5-30}$$

and:

$$\text{Var}(U_T) \doteq \frac{\left[E\left(\sum\limits_{j=1}^{n} T_{s_j} + c \right) \right]^2}{\left[E\left(\sum\limits_{j=1}^{n} \bar{t}_{a_j} P_j \right) \right]^2} \cdot \frac{\text{Var}\left(\sum\limits_{j=1}^{n} T_{s_j} + c \right)}{\left[E\left(\sum\limits_{j=1}^{n} T_{s_j} + c \right) \right]^2}$$

$$+ \frac{\text{Var}\left(\sum\limits_{j=1}^{n} \bar{t}_{a_j} P_j \right)}{\left[E\left(\sum\limits_{j=1}^{n} t_{a_j} P_j \right) \right]^2} + \text{Var}(m) \qquad \text{Eq. 5-31}$$

THE DETERMINATION OF N_T

The model for N_T, total required number of machines of a specific type or model, can now be written as:

$$N_T = \frac{1}{H_a} f \left(\sum_{j=1}^{n} (\bar{t}_{a_j} P_j), U_T \right)$$

but $f \left(\sum_{j=1}^{n} (\bar{t}_{a_j} P_j), U_T \right)$ is just the probability density function of the product

of $\sum_{j=1}^{n} (\bar{t}_{a_j} P_j)$ and U_T, and:

$$\left[\sum_{j=1}^{n} (\bar{t}_{a_j} P_j) \right] U_T = (m+1) \sum_{j=1}^{n} (\bar{t}_{a_j} P_j) + \sum_{j=1}^{n} T_{s_j} + c \qquad \text{Eq. 5–32}$$

Eq. 5–32 is the sum of two approximately normal distributions and will therefore also be approximately normal. Since $1/H_a$ is a constant and the product of a constant and a normal distribution is normal, the distribution of N_T will also be approximately normal. Combining the parameters of the two summed normal distributions and the constant $(1/H_a)$:

$$\text{Var}(N_T) \doteq \left\{ E(m+1)^2 \text{Var} \sum_{j=1}^{n} (\bar{t}_{a_j} P_j) + E \left(\sum_{j=1}^{n} (\bar{t}_{a_j} P_j) \right)^2 \text{Var}(m) \right.$$

$$\left. + \sum_{j=1}^{n} \left(\frac{E(N_j)}{Q_j} \right)^2 \text{Var}(P_j \bar{t}_j) + \sum_{i=1}^{v} \left(\frac{H_a}{\Delta H_{t_{m_i}}} \right)^2 \text{Var}(\bar{t}_{m_i}) \right\} \left(\frac{1}{H_a} \right)^2 \qquad \text{Eq. 5–33}$$

and:

$$E(N_T) = \frac{1}{H_a} \left\{ \sum_{j=1}^{n} \left[\frac{E(N_j)}{Q_j} E(P_j \bar{t}_{s_j}) \right] + \sum_{i=1}^{v} \left[\frac{H_a}{\Delta H_{t_{m_i}}} E(\bar{t}_{m_i}) \right] \right.$$

$$\left. + \left[E(m+1) \sum_{j=1}^{n} (E(\bar{t}_{a_j} P_j)) \right] \right\} \qquad \text{Eq. 5–34}$$

THE EFFECT OF THE MODEL AS COMPARED TO THE TRADITIONAL FORMULA

The Problem

The traditional formula provides the basis for present machine determination. Comparison of results using this formula and the derived model for an illustrative problem follows.

The problem can be stated as follows. Three sequential operations are all performed on the same machine model. The company expects to work 2000 hours per year, operator's mean performance has been 70 percent of standard, and a use factor of 0.85 is used in machine determination. The following data applies to each operation:

Operation Number	Standard Time per Piece in Hours	Expected Percent Defective From Operation	Estimated Annual Requirements of Good Product From Operation
1	0.013	4	......
2	0.022	2½	......
3	0.009	3	288,000 (2000 gross)

Solution by the Traditional Formula

As noted earlier the traditional formula may be written $N = \dfrac{TP}{HC}$, where T is the time in standard hours, P is the required production per year, H is the expected standard hours per year and C is the use factor. H equal to 2000×0.70, or 1400 standard hours and C equal to 0.85 applies to all operations. P is determined for each operation by dividing the annual requirement of good product by $[1 - (\text{percent defective}/100)]$. Calculating for P, to the nearest tens:

$$P \text{ for operation } 1 = \frac{304{,}520}{0.96} = 317{,}210$$

$$P \text{ for operation } 2 = \frac{296{,}910}{0.975} = 304{,}520$$

$$P \text{ for operation } 3 = \frac{288{,}000}{0.97} = 296{,}910$$

Substituting the values above and the standard times per operation into the formula provide the following individual operation requirements:

$$\text{For operation 1; } N_1 = \frac{0.013(317{,}210)}{1400(0.85)} = 3.465$$

$$\text{For operation 2; } N_2 = \frac{0.022(304{,}520)}{1400(0.85)} = 5.630$$

$$\text{For operation 3; } N_3 = \frac{0.009(296{,}910)}{1400(0.85)} = 2.246$$

Total machine requirements, N_T, is equal to the sum of requirements for individual operations or 11.341. By normal convention the next higher number of machines, or 12, would be provided.

Solution by the Probabilistic Model

To arrive at the required number of machines by the proposed model the expressions for the mean and variance must be determined. From the traditional model, $E(P_j) = P$, $\bar{t}_{a_j} = T/$(average operator performance), and $H_a = 2000$. Other input values for each operation must be determined. $\bar{t}_{m1} = 2.05$ minutes for daily lubrication with $\Delta H_{t_{m1}} = 8$ hours. Electrical preventive maintenance and mechanical preventive maintenance operations occur every three months. Letting $\bar{t}_{m2} = 78.5$ minutes for electrical and 135.7 minutes $= \bar{t}_{m3}$ for mechanical the corresponding $\Delta H_{t_{m2}}$ and $\Delta H_{t_{m4}}$ can be taken as 500 hours or one-quarter year. Standard time for set-up is 1 hour 30 minutes and average time using the same performance as for operators equal $90/0.7 = 128.7$ minutes. An estimate of m is taken as 0.14 by which the ratio of mean annual maintenance time will be approximately equal to $1 - C$, and thereby provide a better comparison between the two methods of machine determination under similar conditions.

Using the results of the research of Abruzzi and Gomberg the coefficients of variation for the preventive maintenance and setup mean time is taken as 0.03. Note that by so doing the effect of variation is small. If the coefficients of variation were larger, any discrepancies between the proposed and traditional models will also be larger.

As an estimate of N_j for each operation we use the individual operation machine requirements as determined by the traditional model. To estimate Q_j we determine the economic production lot size assuming a unit value of \$0.50, storage and carrying charges equal to 25 percent of inventory value, and order placement cost of \$28. Using a simplified economic lot size quantity formula[5]:

$$Q = \sqrt{\frac{AD}{KB}}$$

where:

 $A = $ Order cost
 $D = $ Annual usage
 $K = $ Annual carrying charge as fraction of value
 $B = $ Unit value.

To find the quantity to start add the expected loss during manufacturing, rounding off to 1000's. Values are collected in Table 5–1. $E(N_i)$ has been taken as the number of machines for operation, i, as determined by the traditional formula and the coefficient of variation for production operation times is taken as 0.1. Also note that the variance of P_j is estimated as $Qp_p(1 - p_p)$. Since the variance of P_j is based upon the expected input quantity to the system Q, assumed constant, and the estimated fraction defective for prior operations, p_p, then $\mathrm{Var}(P_1)$ would be zero for the model.

---

[5] G. B. Carson (ed.), *Production Handbook*, (2d ed.; New York: The Ronald Press Co., 1958). For a fuller treatment of lot size formulas see James H. Greene, *Operations Planning and Control* (Irwin Series in Operations Management [Homewood, Ill.: Richard D. Irwin, Inc., 1967]), chap. 4.

TABLE 5–1
Input Values for Example of Model Results

Variable   Value

H_a   2,000   hours
$E(P_1)$ 317,210
$E(P_2)$ 304,520
$E(P_3)$ 296,910
$\bar{t}_{a1}$ ....   0.0185   hour
$\bar{t}_{a2}$ ....   0.0314   hour
$\bar{t}_{a3}$ ....   0.0129   hour
$E(t_{s_j})$ ....   2.145   hours
$E(t_{m_1})$ ....   0.034   hour
$E(t_{m2})$ ....   1.308   hours
$E(t_{m3})$ ....   2.262   hours
$\Delta H_{t_{m1}}$ 8   hours
$\Delta H_{t_{m2}}$ 500   hours
$\Delta H_{t_{m3}}$ 500   hours
m 0.14

$\text{Var} \sum\limits_{j=1}^{n} (\bar{t}_{aj}P_j) = 344379 +$
$\qquad\qquad 886485 + 146012 =$ 1,376,876
$\text{Var}(m)$ 0.04
$\text{Var}(P_1\bar{t}_{s_1})$ 416,576,670
$\text{Var}(P_2\bar{t}_{s_2})$ 383,968,305
$\text{Var}(P_3\bar{t}_{s_3})$ 365,052,970
$\text{Var}(\bar{t}_{m_1})$ .... 1.96×10^{-6}
$\text{Var}(\bar{t}_{m_2})$ 0.0015
$\text{Var}(\bar{t}_{m_3})$ 0.0046
$\text{Var}(\bar{t}_{s_j})$ 0.00414
$E(N_1)$ 3.465
$E(N_2)$ 5.630
$E(N_3)$ 2.246
Q_1   9,000
Q_2   8,640
Q_3   8,420
$C(\bar{t}_{aj})$ 0.100
$\text{Var}(\bar{t}_1)$ .... 0.34225×10^{-5}
$\text{Var}(P_1)$ 0.0
$\text{Var}(\bar{t}_2)$ 0.95596
$\text{Var}(P_2)$ 12,180.86
$\text{Var}(\bar{t}_3)$ .... 0.16641×10^{-5}
$\text{Var}(P_3)$ 1 9,278.438

Example Results

Applying the values in Table 5–1 and text prior to the equation for $E(N_j)$, the estimate of the mean of the distribution, we obtain the following:

$$E(N_T) = \frac{1}{H_a}\left\{ \sum_{j=1}^{n}\left[\frac{E(N_j)}{Q_j} E(P_j\bar{t}_{s_j}) \right] + \sum_{i=1}^{v}\left[\frac{H_a}{\Delta H_{t_{mi}}} E(\bar{t}_{m_i}) \right] \right.$$

$$+ E(m+1) \sum_{j=1}^{n} \left(E(\bar{t}_{a_j} P_j) \right) \bigg\}$$

$$= \frac{1}{2000} \Bigg\{ \left[\frac{3.465}{9000}(680,415) + \frac{5.63}{8420}(643,195) \right.$$

$$\left. + \frac{2.246}{8420}(529,622) \right] + \left[\frac{2000}{8}(0.032) + \frac{2000}{500}(1.308) \right.$$

$$\left. + \frac{2000}{500}(2.262) \right] + 1.14[5868.39 + 9561.93 + 3830.14] \Bigg\}$$

$$= \frac{1}{2000} \Bigg\{ [261.960 + 419.097 + 141.273] + [8.500$$

$$+ 5.232 + 9.058] + [21956.924] \Bigg\}$$

$$= \frac{1}{2000}(22802.034)$$

$$= 11.401 \text{ machines}$$

$$\text{Var}(N_T) \doteq \frac{1}{(2000)^2} \Bigg\{ [E(m+1)]^2 \text{Var} \left[\sum_{j=1}^{n} (\bar{t}_{a_j} P_j) \right]$$

$$+ \left[E \left(\sum_{j=1}^{n} \bar{t}_{a_j} P_j \right) \right]^2 \text{Var}(m) + \left[\sum_{j=1}^{n} \left(\frac{E(N_j)}{Q_j} \right)^2 \text{Var}(P_j \bar{t}_{a_j}) \right]$$

$$+ \sum_{i=1}^{v} \left(\frac{H_a}{\Delta H_{t_{m_i}}} \right)^2 \text{Var}(\bar{t}_{m_i}) \Bigg\}$$

$$= \frac{1}{(2000)^2} \Bigg\{ [(1.4)^2(1376876)] + [(19260.46)^2(0.04)]$$

$$+ \left[\frac{3.465^2}{9000}(416,576,670) + \frac{5.63^2}{8640}(383,968,305) \right.$$

$$\left. + \left(\frac{2.246}{8420} \right)^2 (365,052,970) \right] + [(250)^2(1.96 \times 10^{-6})$$

$$+ 4^2(0.0015) + 4^2(0.0046)]$$

$$= \frac{1}{(2000)^2}[1789938 + 14838612.776 + 62.748$$

$$+ 162.227 + 26.612 + 0.1225 + 0.0240 + 0.0736]$$

$$= \frac{1}{(2000)^2}(16628802.582) = \frac{16628802.582}{4 \times 10^6}$$

$$= 4.157$$

Standard Deviation $N_T = \sqrt{\mathrm{Var}(N_T)} = 2.04$

THE EFFECT OF THE VARIANCE ON ECONOMIC DECISION

The results by the traditional model for N and by the proposed model for $E(N_T)$ are similar and would be identical if values of the traditional values had been obtained from the detailed input to the probabilistic model. In either case it would be necessary to provide 12 machines to satisfy estimated requirements. However, by the variance factor of the model a further economic decision is possible. To accomplish this, use is made of the Morris decision model.[6] Repeating Morris' decision model with present notation:

$$C_0(N_T) = C_{0_1}N_T + C_{0_2} \int\limits_{N_T}^{\infty} (n_t - N_T)f(n_t)\,dn_t$$

$C_0(N_T) = $ The expected cost of a policy of providing N_T machines

$\quad C_{0_1} = $ Fixed charges per machine per period

$\quad C_{0_2} = $ Cost penalty (excess of regular time) per machine of overtime production

$\quad f(n_t) = $ Probability distribution of actual number of machines required in a period.

The optimum policy is then computed by setting:

$$\frac{dC_0(N_T)}{d(N_T)} = 0$$

The result is a value of N_T taken as $N_T{}^*$, which satisfies the relationship:

$$\int\limits_{0}^{N_T{}^*} f(n_t)\,dn_t = F(N_T{}^*) = \frac{C_{0_2} - C_{0_1}}{C_{0_2}}$$

In the decision model costs are assumed to be linear.

An application of the decision model is now made to the example problem. A plant in Indiana estimates the cost per machine hour on regular time as \$7 and on overtime as \$11. Using these cost values and the mean and variance of N_T obtained above a decision as to the economic number

---

[6] William T. Morris, *Engineering Economy* (Homewood, Ill.: Richard D. Irwin, Inc., 1960).

of machines can be made. Rewriting the decision equation and substituting values for symbols:

$$\int_{0}^{N_T^*} f(n_t)\,dn_t = F(N_T^*) = \frac{C_{O_2} - C_{O_1}}{C_{O_2}} = \frac{11 - 7}{11} = \frac{4}{11} = P\{n_t \leq N_T^*\}$$

The Z value of the standardized normal distribution can be determined:

$$Z = \frac{N_T^* - E(N_T)}{\sqrt{\mathrm{Var}(N_T)}}.$$

At

$$P\{n_t \leq N_T^*\} = \frac{11}{4} = 0.363, Z = -0.35.$$

Substituting:

$$-0.35 = \frac{N_T^* - 11.401}{2.04}$$

$$N_T^* = 11.401 - 0.714 = 10.687\,.$$

The saving in this case under the stated decision rule would be one machine. It should be repeated that variances on operation, maintenance, and setup times were assumed small. Increased variances, an increased value for m, or reduced lot sizes could significantly affect the resultant optimal value of N_T as compared to $E(N_T)$.

THE EFFECT OF VARIANCE ON DECISIONS OF AVAILABILITY

Perhaps another management decision rule as important in many cases as that of optimal economy is the ability to assure sufficient production capacity. This basis of decision is reinforced by the fact that during periods of maximum machine or plant capacity demand costs tend to rise since the minimum operating cost point may be at 85 to 95 percent capacity. By the model, and in fact any of the available models, the resultant expected number of machines assumes a level of production capacity. Furthermore, the economic decision rule of Morris assumes time availability for over-time which may not be true for a plant operating on a 24-hour day. To overcome the effect of these conditions management may wish to provide a statistical confidence of sufficient capacity.

Statistical confidence may be obtained by again applying the Z value to the standardized normally distributed random variable N_T. For any desired confidence the corresponding Z value can be obtained from the tables of the cumulative probabilities of the normal probability distribution. For example, if a confidence level of 0.90 is desired the corresponding Z value of 1.282 can be used to determine the corresponding N_T. For the example data, for:

$$P\{n_t \le N_T\} = 0.90, Z = 1.282$$

and

$$Z = \frac{N_T - E(N_T)}{\sqrt{\text{Var}(N_T)}}$$

Substituting:

$$1.282 = \frac{N_T - 11.401}{2.04}$$

and

$$N_T = 1.282(2.04) + 11.401$$

$$= 2.615 + 11.401$$

$$= 14.016 \text{ machines}$$

At this point another decision must be made as to whether to reduce confidence and provide 14 machines or increase confidence by providing 15 machines.

In the same manner as for the desired confidence of 0.90 the obtainable confidence can be determined. First for $N_T = 14$:

$$Z = \frac{N_T - E(N_T)}{\sqrt{\text{Var}(N_T)}} = \frac{14 - 11.401}{2.04} = \frac{2.599}{2.04} = 1.274$$

and the corresponding confidence level from the cumulative probabilities table is 0.8987. For $N_T = 15$:

$$Z = \frac{N_T - E(N_T)}{\sqrt{\text{Var}(N_T)}} = \frac{15 - 11.401}{2.04} = \frac{3.599}{2.04} = 1.764$$

and the corresponding confidence level is 0.9611.

REVIEW QUESTIONS

1. When considering machine requirements under probabilistic criteria why is it necessary to use average rather than standard times?
2. What is the significance of considering fraction defective at each operation rather than for a total process?
3. What is the significance of grouping limited demand products?
4. Explain the difference between machine utilization and the machine use factor. Why may this be significant in planning machine requirements?
5. Explain the types of maintenance programs which must be considered in machine requirements planning and how these affect planning.
6. How does tooling affect machine requirements planning? What does this imply relative to future technological progress?
7. Name two types of decision situations when probabilistic considerations might be involved. What is the importance of each and why may they indicate conflicting decisions?

PROBLEMS

1. The calculated expected value of requirements for machine type "A" is 7.64 and Var $(N_T) = 6.25$.

   a) If the cost including burden for operating the machine during a regular work shift is \$15 per hour and cost of overtime including reduced efficiency is \$25 per hour, what is the optimum number of machines of type "A" to provide?

   b) If we desire 95 percent confidence that we have production capacity on machines type "A," how many machines are required?

2. a) What is the annual cost of providing 95 percent confidence of having sufficient production capacity in problem 1? (Assume 2000 hours per year.)

   b) Name some other factors which might be important to management in deciding on the number of machines to purchase.

3. Two operations are performed on the same machine type. Operation 1 is expected to be performed 55,000 times per year with a variance of 16,000 and operation 2, 40,000 times with a variance of 9,000. Operation 1 has a standard time of .08 hours and operation 2 a standard of .12 hours. Study has shown performance against standard to be 110 percent with a 10 percent co-efficient of variation. The expected time for set up is two hours for operation 1 and ten hours for operation 2, each with a coefficient of variation of 0.08. The cost of placing a production order is \$35 and annual inventory carrying cost is 25 percent of unit value. Daily equipment maintenance for each machine is expected to require ten minutes and monthly maintenance two hours each with a coefficient of variation of 0.15. If the plant normally operates 250 eight-hour days per year and $m = .2$, find:

   a) $E(N_T)$ and Var (N_T) for the machine type. Unit value of product is \$5.00.

   b) If the cost of straight time is \$12 per hour and if overtime is \$20 per hour, what is the optimum number of machines?

Chapter 6

FLOW AND ARRANGEMENT—GENERAL

AFTER THE DETERMINATION of the number of machines required for the manufacture of a given product mix, it is necessary to arrange the equipment in unit areas of the plant and in turn the unit areas into the total plant. The primary objective of arrangement, whether unit area or total plant, is to progress from unworked materials to shipped product in a systematic manner with minimum backtracking, lowest weight handling distance, and optimum cost.

There are two principle plant arrangement types: process and product.

Process arrangement is the grouping together of like machines according to their operational characteristics. For example, die casting in one department, turret lathes in another department, and milling machines in a third department. Process arrangement is recommended when a number of products are being manufactured—none of which can individually utilize portions of the equipment full time. Under this condition equipment assigned to the manufacture of a single product type would result in excessively low equipment utilization and high investment cost per unit product.

Process arrangement enables optimum scheduling of equipment across a number of products. As a production run for one product is completed, the equipment may be reassigned and scheduled to the production of a second product, reducing idle time of the equipment. It may also facilitate equipment reassignment to reduce the effect of equipment requirement conflicts between products scheduled independently by production control.

Product arrangement on the other hand is the arrangement of equipment based upon the sequence of operations required for the manufacture of an individual product or a group of similar products requiring all or a major part of the same manufacturing equipment in the same sequence. When the quantity required of a single product group is sufficient that all, or an optimum portion of the equipment time can be utilized for its manufacture, it is advantageous to arrange the equipment in such a manner that the handling between successive operations is held to a minimum without backtracking during the process. The probable utilization of equipment under product arrangement is not as high as under process arrangement unless the operation of the line approaches continuous production. The manufacture of a single product or line of product seldom, if ever, provides perfect balance of individual equipment requirements, thereby necessitating some of the equipment assigned to the manufacturing process remaining idle for a portion of the manufacturing period. The duration of these individual idle times in the manufacturing process, however, do not justify the reassignment of the available time to other operations. As a result, the equipment remains idle and utilization is reduced.

Arrangement Flow Patterns

Regardless of whether product arrangement or process arrangement is selected for the general plant pattern, certain considerations should be

FIGURE 6–1

Production Flow Patterns

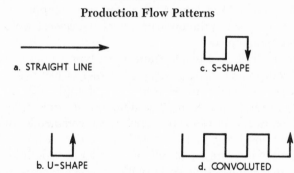

a. STRAIGHT LINE   c. S-SHAPE

b. U-SHAPE   d. CONVOLUTED

given to the nature of the detailed flow patterns within the overall arrangement. Flow patterns may be divided into two types: flow patterns required for production lines; and flow patterns required for assembly lines. Each of these, although they may be integrated within the overall plant arrangement, have somewhat different characteristics.

There are four basic production line flow patterns. These are:

1. Straight-line flow pattern.
2. U-Shaped flow pattern.
3. S-Shaped flow pattern.
4. Convoluted flow pattern.

As mentioned earlier, our objective is to be able to progress constantly in the manufacture of a product with a minimum of backtracking and the

FIGURE 6-2

Assembly Flow Patterns

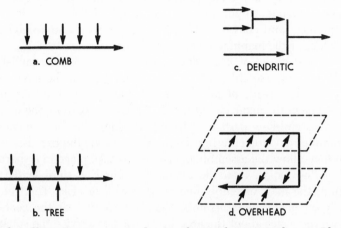

a. COMB

c. DENDRITIC

b. TREE

d. OVERHEAD

shortest handling distance in order to obtain the optimal cost. If we can establish a production line by which we can progress successively from the first machine in the process to the last machine along a straight line, and so long as the distance between those machines is the practical minimum, the total handling distance will be minimal.

It may not be convenient to arrange a building or an area such that we can move in a straight line. Straight-line arrangement could result in a very narrow building or area relative to its length, thereby resulting in inefficiencies insofar as the cost of construction, the cost of supervision, and the cost of providing plant services are concerned. In order to overcome this, we may plan to progress successively from the beginning to the finishing operations without backtracking, but to fold the path so that it approaches a U-shape. Another advantage of the U-flow is that it permits the establishment of receiving and shipping operations on the same side of the area or building so that, from an operational and supervisory standpoint, these can be combined.

If the line is long relative to the building design it is likely a single U is not satisfactory in that space is wasted, or the line is so long that the long narrow building or area of the straight-line arrangement is approached. Therefore, additional loops are required to provide reasonable use of space for supervision and control. If one loop is added it results in the S-shape arrangement. The addition of a greater number of loops results in the convoluted arrangement. Note that regardless of the flow pattern we progress from the first to the last operation along a straight line or a series of straight lines without backtracking, but as loops are added the total distance may increase due to equipment positioning factors.

There may be different basic arrangements in individual production areas—each variation being classified under one of the basic forms. The general flow pattern, on the other hand, may be of another pattern different from that found within any of the individual areas. There should be no attempt made to restrict all production line arrangements within a plant or plant area to one of the basic forms. Keep in mind the flow pattern may be largely dependent upon the size and shape of the available area, and the economical and convenient location of shipping and receiving docks for the plant or the manufacturing area under consideration.

The second group of basic flow patterns are used in establishing the general shape of assembly lines. In the comb pattern the main assembly line is fed from a series of subassembly or parts lines all originating from the same side of the main assembly line. In the tree pattern, the main line is fed by subassembly or parts lines from both sides. For the same number of subassemblies or parts entering the main assembly, the tree assembly line pattern may allow the assembly operations to take place in a shorter main assembly line length than the comb. The comb pattern lends itself to location of the main assembly line along a wall or aisle. The tree is used primarily when the main assembly line is located near the center of an area with the aisles about the area being used to service the subassembly lines.

The dendritic flow pattern is more irregular than either the comb or tree pattern. Each part progresses along its production line until production is completed to the point of assembly, at which time it is combined with other parts to form a subassembly or assembly. The subassembly in turn is combined with other subassemblies or parts to form a more progressive subassembly. The result is that the number of lines along which parts or assemblies are moving are continually reduced as assembly progresses toward the final product.

Regardless of the assembly pattern chosen, it is desirable that before a subassembly moves to the next succeeding assembly operation, the final operation of the subassembly be located as close to the next operation in the total assembly process as possible providing minimum reasonable handling or transportation times. This may significantly affect "through put time" for the product. Since most manufacturing areas or buildings are rectangular, it is often necessary to mesh or organize individual lines of varying lengths to permit optimum area utilization within the constraints of total production system cost and effectiveness. This is illustrated in Figure 6–3.

FIGURE 6–3

Folding Assembly or Production Lines

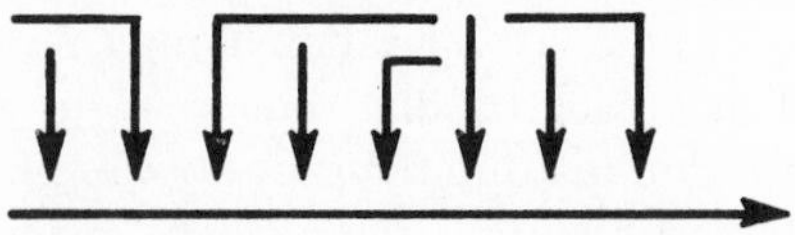

Building Shape Factors

In a new plant the building should be designed to conform to the production flow patterns and assembly flow patterns which optimize the manufacturing process system. In existing plants the flow patterns may have to be altered to conform with existing constraints of building design. It may be possible to change certain wall locations and openings, but the major structural components of the building are usually fixed and cannot be altered economically. The basic building shape is usually a significant component of the manufacturing system and can facilitate the smooth flow of production. Buildings themselves supplement or complement the basic flow pattern design and thereby influence system effectiveness. The building in practically all industrial situations is composed of combinations of rectangular or square areas. The combinations result commonly in buildings of the shapes:

LTUCHFEOI

A square building will have a shorter perimeter per square foot of usable area. This reduction in perimeter length results in lower foundation and outside wall costs. At the same time, however, the square shape of the building often does not lend itself as readily to efficient production or assembly line patterns. Furthermore, the cost of structural steel for floor and roof supports in the square building may exceed that for a rectangular building of the same area and may offset the possible savings in foundation and wall costs. Primarily for these two reasons, the majority of industrial buildings will have a rectangular shape rather than square. Regardless of which shape is selected, the arrangement of the building must facilitate the maximizing of its effectiveness for manufacture of the product mix.

Machine Arrangement Patterns

In all cases, flow patterns within a building are dependent upon: (1) the available floor area, (2) the dimensions of the floor area, and (3) the individual machine or work station area requirements. Machine area requirements in turn may be dependent upon individual machine contours. Work station area must also include area requirements for the operator, incoming materials, in-process materials, outgoing materials, tools, jigs, fixtures, machine and operation setup, and area for maintenance performed at the work station.

Machine arrangements may be classified into four general patterns. First, the *straight-line machine arrangement* in which the main axis of the machine follows the main axis of the adjacent aisle. In arranging machines

FIGURE 6–4

Machine Arrangement

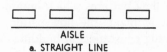

AISLE
a. STRAIGHT LINE

⊗ OPERATOR
c. CIRCULAR

AISLE
b. DIAGONAL

d. ODD-ANGLE

in straight-line patterns, the normal procedure is to have an aisle, two rows of machines each parallel to the aisle with the operator either facing toward or away from the aisle, and then another aisle. This results in the total number of aisles required being equal to one half the number of machine rows.

The second machine arrangement is *diagonal* represented by the center line of the machine being placed at some angle to the direction of the aisle. The diagonal arrangement permits servicing of the machine in such a manner that materials may arrive from one direction on one side of the machine, and leave the machine areas on the other side of the machine with handling equipment travel opposite to that of the first aisle. This is more likely to result in efficient use of one-way traffic and thereby may reduce aisle width requirements. Narrower aisles may also be used due to reduced turning area required for the handling equipment. No longer must the equipment make a full 90 degree turn in order to drop or pick up a load. The third advantage of the diagonal arrangement over the straight-line arrangement is that for a given area the number of machines that can be placed in the area may be increased. This results from machines normally being longer than they are wide. Placing the machine length diagonal to the aisle allows more machines along the length of the aisle reducing the number of aisles required for a given number of machines, thereby increasing the proportional amount of area assignable to machines and reducing that assignable to aisles.

The third basic machine arrangement is the *circular arrangement.* The circular arrangement is advantageous when it is possible for one operator to care for a number of machines. In a circular arrangement, the machines are placed about the circumference of a circular pattern with the operator at its center. The operator moves along the circumference of the machine circle servicing each machine in its turn or as required. Both analytic and simulation (Monte Carlo) techniques are available to determine the number of machines which should be assigned to the individual operator or crew.

The fourth basic machine arrangement is the *odd-angle arrangement.* In odd-angle arrangement, each machine is arranged such that it can most conveniently receive materials or parts from the preceding machine and pass them to the suceeding machine. The advantages of the odd-angle arrangement are that it permits the shortest travel and minimum area for a given number of machines. It requires less total area due to the fact that machines may be arranged in such a manner that the contour of one machine is matched with the contour of another machine to reduce void areas to a practical minimum. Odd-angle arrangement best facilitates automation in that short distances are involved between machines and production parts can be automatically removed from one machine, moved to the next position, and loaded on the second machine with minimum transfer time or in-process storage between successive operations.

Within the finalized arrangement pattern, aisles must be provided for movement of personnel, materials, and equipment. After the traffic level is established, the aisle width must permit movement of materials without creating safety hazardous conditions for personnel involved in cross traffic or using adjacent aisles or work areas. To assure safety, personnel aisles should be designated and maintained separate from aisles used for the movement of materials by color coding stripping on the floor defining that area reserved for personnel. When considering aisles, main aisles should be minimized. Area is valuable and an excess of area in wide major aisles reduces the area assignable to profit producing production activities.

FUTURE EXPANSION

It may be desirable during arrangement planning to provide for future expansion of either production or total plant facilities. Provision may be made for expansion either upward or outward. In modern industry new plants tend to be located on larger lots, permitting outward expansion. In these cases it may not be necessary to make provision in the original planning for upward expansion. Expansion upward normally increases the handling problem and necessitates a complete rearrangement of a large portion of the existing manufacturing facilities. This is expensive and is to be avoided unless the manufacturing process is facilitated in so doing. In planning the arrangement plan the flow in such a manner as to permit expansion at a later date with minimum expansion cost, minimum re-arrangement and relocation of existing equipment, and minimum lost production time. Where individual production lines are used provision may be made for future expansion by planning the addition of new lines parallel to presently existing lines within the present building or within new facilities. This approach is frequently found in steam power electric generating plant planning. Under process arrangement, the departments may be arranged such that individual departments or groups of departments can be expanded outward from their initial location without revision and rearrangement of the total original layout. Only certain departments may require disruption and relocation rather than change in all departments. In planning the arrangement anticipate the first few additions and plan accordingly. Decisions as to the extent of, and timing of, future expansion may be anticipated and taken into consideration during initial planning through the use of forecasting, capital assignment, and decision models.

Thought must be given, during the initial design of the building, to the maximum height requirements for manufacturing equipment or manufacturing process. Clear ceiling heights, taking into consideration utilities and sprinkler distribution systems required clearance, must be designated to meet these requirements. If a limited number of machines or other types of equipment require higher ceilings than the bulk of the equipment, these taller machines may be placed in separate bays or buildings with the required high ceilings. Building areas for normal equipment can then be constructed with somewhat lower ceilings. Scattering tall machines throughout the manufacturing area will increase the total cost of the building above that which is economical with planned wall and columnar heights. Automated or high rack storage should be considered for high bay sections. Total system cost models should be evaluated carefully in planning the location of multiple high bay or heavy floor loading areas.

The third major building shape and structural limitation is floor loading. Floor loading is particularly important when multiple-story buildings are being considered due to the hazards created on the lower floors from overloading an upper floor. Before finalizing the layout it should be determined by conference with the structural engineer and the architect that no dangerous floor loading conditions are created by the desired layout. Furthermore, during expansion or relayout of existing plants when heavy equipment is being relocated, it is paramount that the determination be made as to whether floor capacity is sufficient to support the material and/or equipment with a satisfactory safety factor during use. Heavy equipment should be located on the ground floor. Structural alterations or designs can then be incorporated to provide special supports and foundations only at those points necessitating them rather than throughout the entire structure.

Sufficient planning must be given to the design of flow patterns to coordinate the overall process and the individual areas within the process. The flow pattern selected will determine the cost of flow of materials, assemblies and personnel throughout the plant area, and provide coordinated relationships for the total plant system design. In the final analysis the plant integrated system can be no better than the flow pattern of materials and information established by the arrangement of the machines and equipment required to fulfill the process design.

REVIEW QUESTIONS

1. Name and distinguish between the two principal types of plant arrangement. Which tends to facilitate scheduling? Machine utilization?
2. What are the four basic production line flow patterns? What common characteristic do they all have?
3. What are the basic patterns for arranging assembly? When might you want to use each?
4. Name and indicate the significance of the principal factors influencing flow patterns.
5. Name, illustrate, and indicate when each of the general machine arrangement patterns might be used.
6. How may future expansion be allowed for in building planning? What factors or building characteristics may restrict expansion?
7. How may ceiling height and floor loading affect initial and long range costs to the firm?

Chapter 7

SYSTEMATIC PLANT ARRANGEMENT— TECHNIQUES AND MODELS

THE PLANT ARRANGEMENT is a system composed of interacting individual departments (themselves subsystems with work stations as components) and to a significant degree determines the firm's effectiveness in being able to fulfill major objectives. To systematically arrive at an arrangement first consider the combination of production departments into necessary plant manufacturing areas. After the combination of manufacturing departments, add the complementary or supplementary departments and their required office areas necessary for the manufacturing facilities. These last include, but may not be limited to, production control, inventory and materials control, quality control, storerooms, stock rooms, shipping, receiving, tool rooms, engineering, and plant maintenance. To manufacturing related departments add general business departments such as accounting, sales, purchasing, personnel, and administrative offices to complete the plant system.

PROCEDURAL TECHNIQUES FOR PLANT ARRANGEMENT

There are several means by which we can procedurally determine the arrangement of departments within the plant. Three of these are representative:[1]

---

[1] For a complete discussion of these methods see Ruddell Reed, Jr., *Plant Layout* (Homewood, Ill.: Richard D. Irwin, Inc., 1961).

1. Spiral analysis.
2. Straight-line analysis.
3. Travel charting.

While none of these are quantitative in nature, they provide a quantitative evalution of relationships between alternative arrangements of the departments within the total area. The discussion of these methods is directly related to arrangement of departments within the plant. However, they can also be used for determining the relative position of individual machines or machine groups within a department. While it is convenient to discuss the techniques relative to departments within the plant, keep in mind the principles involved are general enough to be applied to work stations within departments.

In considering arrangement our concern will not be with product type arrangements, but rather with process type arrangements. The reason for this is that if the product mix is sufficiently similar that a product arrangement can be used throughout the plant, the primary problem becomes line balancing (to be discussed later) followed by arrangement. Under product arrangement each department should have work stations arranged as close to a straight-line sequence as reasonable. The lines representing different products will then tend to be parallel to one another.

It is common that a combination of process and product arrangement is utilized. In these cases a number of products or product types may utilize available time on the equipment within certain departments while other departments are product oriented. Under these conditions it is necessary to arrange the product departments by line balancing after which they are combined with the process department by process arrangement techniques. The following semiquantitative techniques for plant arrangement are applicable to these mixed situations as well as to pure process arrangements.

It should also be noted that analogous statements relative to process versus product department arrangements are applicable to production service and business service operations as well as manufacturing. The techniques and models which follow are therefore general in their applicability.

Spiral Method of Plant Arrangement

Before discussing the spiral method of arrangement analysis we establish a set of conditions representing the activity mix such as those indicated in Figure 7–1. Note the manner in which the data is presented. In the left-hand column is listed the product groups by number. Each group may represent a product or group of products which follow the manufacturing sequence by departments as shown in the right-hand column where each letter designates an individual department. Though materials may arrive

FIGURE 7-1

Sequence and Area Required for Processing Departments

Product Group	% Volume	Production Sequence by Departments
I.........................	17.1	Stores *ABCDEF* Stock
II........................	11.8	Stores *BDEF* Stock
III.......................	28.3	Stores *ABDCF* Stock
IV.......................	23.2	Stores *BCDCEF* Stock
V........................	8.3	Stores *BCDE* Stock
Total..................	88.7	

Department	Required Area in Sq. Ft.
A...............................	600
B...............................	900
C...............................	1000
D...............................	700
E...............................	1100
F...............................	1500
Stores	1200
Stock............................	900
Total..........................	7900

at the first operation directly from outside sources or may leave the final operation for the customer, methods must be provided in the materials control system whereby items received will be inspected and/or accounted for, and those completed inspected, accounted for, and invoiced before forwarding. The first and/or last step in the sequence under these conditions is analogous to stores and stock accountability with minimum materials delay.

The objective of the spiral method is to arrange individual areas to obtain the most direct flow of materials between successive steps in the sequence table. The area required in the unit area normally will vary only slightly as the arrangement is changed, assuming the initial arrangement is logical. Furthermore, the area of a department will vary only slightly as the peripheral shape of that department is changed so long as the department shape is a combination of square or rectangular areas. Under these two assumptions, the objective is to determine the relationship of unit areas (position and to a lesser extent shape) within the total available area. The steps involved in the spiral procedural analysis are:

1. Draw a circle to represent each department or activity area.
2. On the left side of the circle draw a line to represent incoming material from each activity which immediately precedes the activity of interest for any product group.
3. On each line to the circle indicate the quantity or percent of total activity between the two sequence steps.

4. At the right of the circle draw a connecting line which denotes each disposition of materials completed.
5. Designate on these lines the quantity or percent of total activity represented by the completed material.

The five steps result in a schematic representation of activity levels involving the activity represented by the circle. These steps are completed for all activities. To minimize handling distances and thereby handling activity between departments, each department should be so located that at least a portion of its boundary be adjacent to each of the departments from which it receives materials and to which it delivers materials. If this can be accomplished the material being worked on upon completion can be moved to the next succeeding area at minimum handling cost. The problem is to arrange the individual activity areas such that the boundary of each area is common to each of its servicing or serviced areas while at the same time assuring the area requirement of the individual activity areas are satisfied:

6. By trial and error start with the first activity area and locate it in such a manner that the serviced areas and servicing areas are located around its periphery.
7. Around each of the service activity areas arrange their servicing or serviced areas in turn, again maintaining the necessary area assignment for each.

Continue the process until all activity areas have been located in such a manner that to the extent possible a common boundary exists between each of the activity areas and those areas which are either serviced by, or are servicing, the area under consideration.

It will be noted that this is a trial and error procedure. There is no assurance under the procedure that the optimum solution has been obtained. Spirals for the data of Figure 7–1 are given in Figure 7–2. A possible arrangement is represented in Figure 7–3.

Straight-Line Arrangement Method

In the straight-line method of arrangement the objective again is to reduce the total handling distance-volume of product and goods flowing through the manufacturing area to the practical minimum. If departments are arranged in such a manner that each product or product group flowing through the departments can move in a straight line from beginning to completion of operations the total handling distance will approach a minimum. The following steps may be used in planning arrangement by the straight-line method:

1. In addition to the sequential data used for the spiral method, determine the relative volume for each of the products or product classes moving through the area. See Figure 7–1. Note that in the example data the total

FIGURE 7-2

Spiral Analysis of Each Department's Relationship
with Other Departments

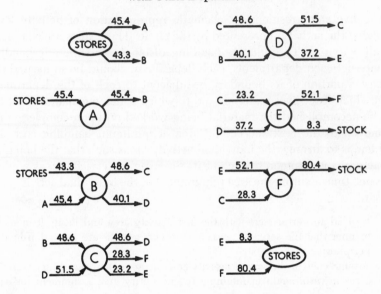

NOTE: Except for stores and stocks the total number of product groups entering the department must be equal to the total number leaving. Variation indicates error in spiral preparation.

FIGURE 7-3

A Feasible Arrangement for Figure 7-1 Data by the
Spiral Method

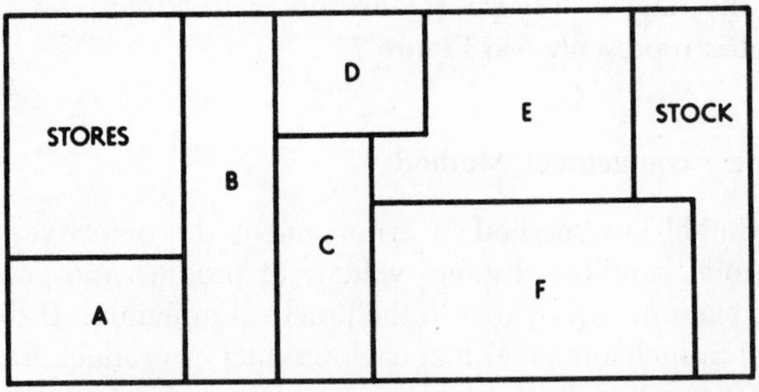

volume of the product groups under consideration is less than 100 percent. Frequently a limited number of products or product groups account for the major portion of production. The remaining portion of production is made up of products which collectively do not have significant affect on the total production pattern. (This is a similar condition to an ABC inventory system where "C" type inventories may contain 50 percent of the items but only 5 percent of the value.) Volume may be expressed in number of handling loads, number of containers, tons, or other measure which establishes a relative measure of demand on production facilities.

2. Determine the area required for each of the processing departments to be included in the analysis.

3. Using the total area requirement, establish the shape and preliminary dimensions of the building, indicating column spacing where necessary, and the direction of flow of parts. This flow direction along a straight line may be represented by a series of parallel lines each designated as one of the product groups flowing from left to right of the preliminary building or production area shape. This is indicated in Figure 7–4. Note that the

FIGURE 7–4

Tentative Location of Product Group Production Lines

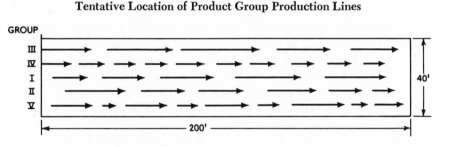

parallel lines progress from the highest percent volume product group to the next higher percent product group, and so forth, until all groups have been located.

4. Establish relative positions of lines through the area, progressively from the line of maximum volume to the line of minimum volume. This does not assure proper positions. To improve product line sequence, prepare a cross-reference matrix similar to that of Figure 7–5 indicating by percentage or production quantity the volume of each product which passes through each of the manufacturing departments.

FIGURE 7–5

Cross–Reference Matrix of Product Group
versus Processing Department

| Product | Stores | *Percent of Total Product Passing through Department* | | | | | | |
		A	B	C	D	E	F	Stock
III.......	28.3	28.3	28.3	(28.3)	28.3	...	28.3	28.3
IV.......	23.2	...	23.2	23.2 (23.2)	23.2	23.2	23.2	23.2
I.......	17.1	17.1	17.1	17.1	17.1	17.1	17.1	17.1
II.......	11.8	...	(11.8)	...	11.8	11.8	11.8	11.8
V.......	8.3	...	8.3	8.3	8.3	8.3	...	8.3

Circled values in Figure 7–5 indicate backtracking of material. Note in Figure 7–5 the total volume of material moving backward to *C* from succeeding departments exceeds that from preceding departments, indicating that D and C should be interchanged in sequence. A further check of the total system, however, shows that in this particular case the change of arrangement sequence of C and D actually results in increasing the system backtracking. (This points out the necessity of systems analysis for system optimization rather than individual component optimization.) Therefore, the sequence of departments along the product flow lines is maintained as indicated in Figure 7–5. Analysis can now be made as to whether the product lines order from maximum to minimum along the vertical dimension of the layout sketch is proper. Observe the necessary relationships of production departments to satisfy the product groups. For example, note for product II there is no requirement for processing through department C. This would indicate in the layout that a gap or a break in the department is necessary unless product V flow line is placed adjacent to product I. In order to do this, it creates a necessity for department F area to be split. Since there is approximately 40 percent more material being handled for product II than for product V, changing the relationship of product flow sequences would tend to increase the amount of material flowing through a split department. Therefore, the decision is made to maintain the relative positions of the product line as indicated in Figures 7–4 and 7–5. The attempt at this point should be to maintain those products adjacent which will necessitate minimum splitting or unnecessarily stretching out of process departments areas. Noting the preceding four steps:

5. Superimpose a bar graph type representation of the processing departments upon the area layout. This is indicated in Figure 7–6. Note that if there is no requirement for a department in the product sequence the bar is split at that department. This is illustrated by department C in product II and by department A in product IV. In all other cases, the bar extends uninterrupted along the full product flow.

FIGURE 7–6

Bar Chart Representation of Product Lines Served
by Processing Departments

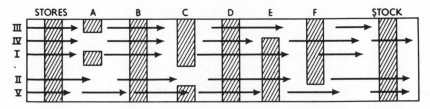

The problem remains to design department shapes and arrangements to assure that available manufacturing area is utilized to maximize the effectiveness of the manufacturing process. A feasible arrangement resulting from application of the straight-line method to the data of Figure 7–1 is shown in Figure 7–7.

FIGURE 7–7

Departmental Arrangement to Satisfy Production Conditions of Figure 7–1 by Straight-Line Method

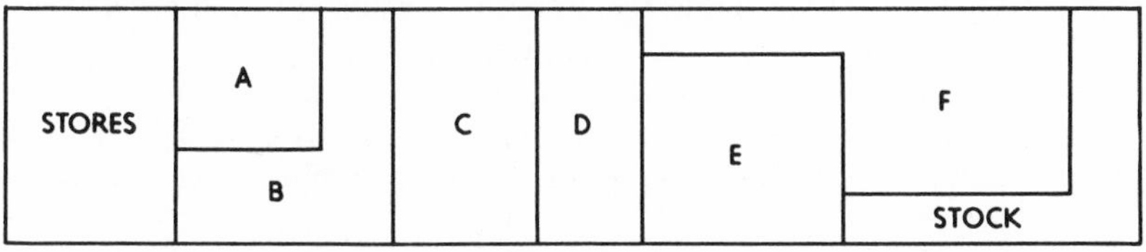

NOTE: *A* and *C* extend across flow lines for which they are not used. In this case the additional handling was considered minor compared to supervision problems created by departmental splitting.

Travel Charting Method

Travel charting may be used for any plant arrangement when product characteristics do not allow the establishment of production lines for individual products or product types.

The procedure for using travel charting is:

1. Collect data as to the volume of handling and the sequence of handling operations by product classes or groups in the same manner as the straight-line method.
2. Prepare a preliminary layout selecting a general flow pattern applicable to the amount and limits of area available.
3. Prepare a distance-volume matrix from the preliminary layout. This may be accomplished by developing separate matrices for distance and volume from which the distance-volume matrix can be obtained by multiplication of identically positioned cells of the initial matrices.
4. Determine critical moves of the preliminary layout in the distance-volume matrix. Critical points are most often those moves of high distance-volume value which are some distance from the chart diagonal. (This is only a guide in locating critical points.)
5. Evaluate critical moves. This involves evaluation of the effect of changing location of departments included in the critical moves. The objective is to reduce the sum of row sums of the distance-volume matrix.
6. Revise distance-volume matrix and plant arrangement until further improvement is insignificant or undeterminable. These revisions may be of two types: revision of the basic flow pattern by trading positions of department areas or redesign of layout area shapes.

To illustrate the application of this procedure assume the following conditions: A plant, producing a series of products, finds after study that its handling problem is represented by the data of Figure 7–1. It is also found that the area required for each department including intradepartmental handling but excluding interdepartmental handling is as shown in Figure 7–1. Aisle width for interdepartment materials handling is 10 feet and the maximum plant area is limited to 70 feet wide and 135 feet long.

It is now necessary to attack the problem by the procedure outlined previously:

Step 1. Collection of the data describing the handling problem is given in Figure 7–1. This table establishes the volume of each product group and the sequence of operations required for its production.

Step 2. An initial departmental arrangement in the allotted total area was prepared. The department arrangement of this first trial is shown in Figure 7–8. Assumption of a common interdepartment aisle running

FIGURE 7–8
First Travel Chart Arrangement

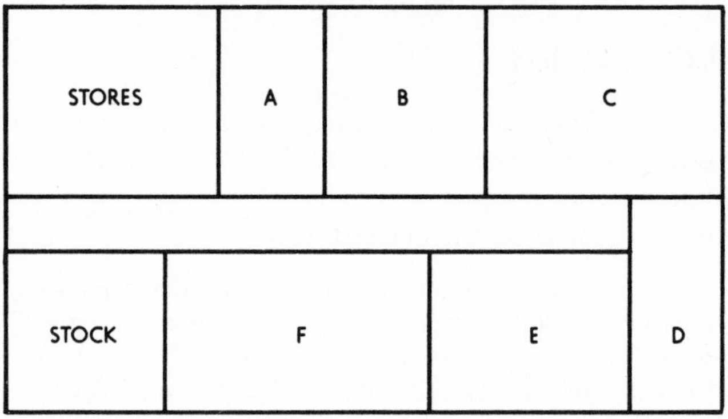

along the center of the area allows receiving and shipping to be located at the same end of the building.

Step 3. The distance-volume matrix for this arrangement is shown in Figure 7–9. It was assumed that average handling to and from each department would be over a path along the main aisle and perpendicular to the main aisle between department centers. Work sampling, simulation queuing, or other techniques can be used to accurately weight intradeparmental handling, if desired. This does not change the basic problem.

Step 4. The critical points determined from observation, considering distance-volume and deviation from basic flow path, are circled in the distance-volume matrix.

Step 5. Evaluation of critical points, C to F and F to stock, indicate a probable improvement if the distances can be reduced through rearrangement. Note that the sum of rows and columns on the distance-volume matrix are equal and this value is the total distance-volume handled. This value is assumed to have a direct relationship to cost. Therefore, our evaluation of arrangement is based upon reducing this value to a minimum.

FIGURE 7–9

Volume, Distance, and Distance–Volume Matrices
for First Travel Chart Arrangement

Volume Matrix

To: Stores	A	B	C	D	E	F	Stock
From:							
Stores	45.4	43.3	...	...	...	...	...
A	...	45.4	...	...	...	...	...
B	...	...	48.6	40.1	...	...	...
C	...	...	...	48.6	23.2	28.3	...
D	...	...	51.5	...	37.2	...	...
E	...	...	...	...	...	52.1	8.3
F	...	...	...	...	...	...	80.4
Stock	...	...	...	...	...	...	...

Distance Matrix

To: Stores	A	B	C	D	E	F	Stock
From:							
Stores	70	95	...	...	...	...	...
A	...	65	...	...	...	...	...
B	...	...	75	85	...	...	...
C	...	...	...	50	55	95	...
D	...	...	50	...	65	...	...
E	...	...	...	...	...	80	120
F	...	...	...	...	...	...	80
Stock	...	...	...	...	...	...	...

Distance–Volume Matrix*

To: Stores	A	B	C	D	E	F	Stock	Total
From:								
Stores	3178	4114	...	...	...	...	...	7292
A	...	3051	...	...	...	...	...	3051
B	...	...	3645	3409	...	...	...	7054
C	...	...	...	2430	1276	(2689)	...	6395
D	...	...	2575	...	2418	...	...	4993
E	...	...	...	...	...	4168	996	5164
F	...	...	...	...	...	...	(6432)	6432
Stock	...	...	...	...	...	...	...	...
Total	3178	7165	6220	5839	3694	6857	7428	46381

* Obtained by multiplying volume and distance matrices cell by cell.

Step 6. A new layout (Figure 7–10) was prepared with the revised arrangement as indicated by Step 5. Steps 3, 4, and 5 were repeated, giving the results indicated in Figures 7–11 and 7–12.

Layout II results in an improvement of 23 percent over the original arrangement of layout I. In an installation with heavy materials handling requirements this could represent a significant portion of total product cost.

FIGURE 7-10

Layout II

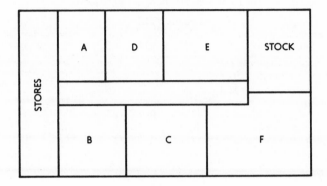

FIGURE 7-11

Distance Matrix—Layout II

To:	Stores	A	B	C	D	E	F	Stock
From:								
Stores	39	44	...	..	..	....	..	
A	..	45	...	..	..	....	..	
B	..	..	72.5	60	..	....	..	
C	..	..	...	55	56	77½	..	
D	..	..	55	..	71	....	..	
E	..	..	...	..	..	61½	70	
F	..	..	...	..	..	....	50	
Stock	..	..	...	..	..	....	..	

NOTE: Volume matrix remains constant.

FIGURE 7-12

Distance–Volume Matrix—Layout II

To:	Stores	A	B	C	D	E	F	Stock	Total
From:									
Stores	1771	1905	....	....	....	....	....	3676	
A	....	2033	....	....	....	....	....	2033	
B	....,	....	3524	2406	....	....	....	5930	
C	....	....	....	2673	1299	2193	....	6165	
D	....	....	2833	....	2641	....	....	5474	
E	....	....	....	....	....	3204	581	3785	
F	....	....	....	....	....	....	4020	4020	
Stock	....	....	....	....	....	....	....	.....	
Total	1771	3938	6357	5079	3940	5397	4601	31,083	

Layout II also points up the fallacy of assuming the relationship between two departments to remain constant. Even though there may have
been validity in maintaining receiving and shipping adjacent, the added

handling cost created could not be recognized unless arrangement II had been developed and evaluated. Note also that layout II reduces total required area.

This illustration points out a significant application of travel charting to relayout problems. Relayout is the most common assignment of the layout planner and frequently involves rearrangement to arrive at the most efficient relationship of facilities within a specific available area. These are basically the conditions established for the illustration previously given in which the application of travel charting resulted in significant improvement. Whenever alternate arrangements are possible and volumes for various production sequences are known or can be reasonably well estimated, travel charting can be used to determine the best of the alternatives.

The technique of travel charts indicates critical points in any particular arrangement pattern, allowing the planner to concentrate his efforts at the points most likely to provide improvement. It does not, however, offer a means of determining the optimum arrangement, but various arrangements which are arrived at can be evaluated on a quantitative basis relative to one another. For this reason, it is a valuable technique. Of the procedural methods travel charting is probably the best due to the variety of situations in which it can be effectively applied.

REVIEW QUESTIONS

1. Establish and justify a sequence for systematically arranging departments or areas to arrive at a total plant arrangement.
2. Indicate the initial design element for spiral, straight-line, and travel charting arrangement techniques. Give the measurement unit for production factors for each technique, and the differences and similarities between the techniques.
3. What are the steps in applying:
   a) The spiral technique?
   b) The straight-line technique?
   c) Travel charting?
4. Why is backtracking to be avoided if possible in plant arrangement?
5. Which of the arrangement techniques appears to have the widest application? Why?

PROBLEMS

1. Given:

Product Group	% Volume	Production Sequence by Departments
I	30	A B C D E
II	15	A D C D E
III	12	A B D E
IV	25	A C B C E

Area requirements:

Department	Required Area in Sq. Ft.
Department A	1000
Department B	1600
Department C	1200
Department D	2000
Department E	1000

Arrange the departments in a building 75 feet by 100 feet, using:

a) Spiral method
b) Straight line method
c) Travel charting

2. a) Using the data of problem 1, with a main aisle in the center of the building parallel to the 100-foot dimension, estimate the relative volume distance using conveyor (department "X" center to department "Q" center) handling versus truck handling (department "X" center to main aisle to department "Y" center) by travel charting.

b) If a single truck can do all handling at an equivalent cost of $3,000 per year, what is the maximum equivalent annual cost per foot of conveyor you can afford?

c) The cost in (b) is only equipment. What effects would you expect from labor costs and why?

Chapter **8**

QUANTITATIVE PROCESS
ARRANGEMENT
TECHNIQUES

A NUMBER of techniques have been proposed to design arrangements by quantitative methods. However, in all cases special conditions must exist in the problem before the optimization method of the individual technique can be applied. Usually these conditions cannot be satisfied in the real world. Even though the special conditions cannot be satisfied, the assumption of these conditions may permit the layout planner to develop a theoretical arrangement which, with minor adjustments for the real world, will provide an arrangement which is near optimum under the specified conditions. For this reason and due to their adaptability to computer solution the quantitative techniques are important.

R. J. Wimmert proposed one of the earliest quantitative techniques.[1] Wimmert uses the criteria of minimized distance-volume of materials handling between departments or machine locations as his criteria. Other criteria are adaptable, but in general the distance-volume criteria appears to be more satisfactory than other criteria not only for Wimmert's method but for other methods. The distance-volume criteria lends itself more readily to cost conversion (which is also dependent upon handling method) than either distance or volume alone.

Three basic assumptions are made by Wimmert's method: (1) individual areas are interchangeable; (2) the distance between two locations is independent of the direction of movement, e.g., distance from i to j is equal to the distance from j to i; and (3) cost is directly proportional to

---

[1] R. J. Wimmert, "A Quantitative Approach to Equipment Location in Intermittent Manufacturing" (Ph.D. thesis, Purdue University, 1957).

equivalent distance. The first of these assumptions is highly restrictive in practice since variation (usually significant) exists between department or machine areas. The second assumption can usually be satisfied in practice. The third assumption may be satisfactory for a single material handling equipment type, but comparison of alternative equipment is questionable.

To illustrate Wimmert's method we will assume we have four departments to be located in four available equal size areas.[2] Selection of a four department problem permits illustration of the technique and limits the number of possible location combinations. There are $N!$ feasible load-distance combinations with one and only one department associated with each location. With four departments $4! = 24$ feasible combinations. If the number of departments increases, the feasible combinations increase rapidly and will likely necessitate use of a computer for solution, for example, an eight department problem will have $8! = 40,320$ combinations.

To use the method a distance matrix and load matrix are first established. Letting D be the load matrix in which cells d_{ij} are distances between locations i and j:

	Location No.	1	2	3	4
$D = (d_{ij}) =$	1	0	42	14	22
	2		0	30	20
	3			0	10
	4				0

The unit period level of product flow between departments is determined as shown in the following matrix, P, in which p_{ij} is the department-directional volume movement in common measurement units, preferably unit load moves:

			To Machine			
			A	B	C	D
$P = (p_{ij}) =$		A	0	40	70	20
	From	B	15	0	45	50
	Machine	C	65	50	0	70
		D	30	32	60	0

Since an initial assumption was that the distance between departments was independent of the direction of movement, we can develop the triangular matrix L to represent the nondirectional total flow between machines from P:

---

[2] This is the same size problem as used in R. J. Wimmert, "A Mathematical Method of Equipment Location," *Journal of Industrial Engineering* (November–December, 1958), p. 498.

	Machine	A	B	C	D
$L = (l_{ij}) =$	A	0	55	135	50
	B		0	95	82
	C			0	130
	D				0

We can now construct a load-distance matrix from the D and L matrices. In order to perform problem solution operations on this matrix later it is necessary that paths between locations ij be used as column headings arranged in nondescending order, left to right, and that loads handled between locations ij be the row headings in nonascending order, top to bottom. Following these restrictions the load-distance matrix is:

TABLE 8–1

Load–Distance Matrix

Machine i–j	Loads between i and j	3–4	1–3	2–4	1–4	2–3	1–2	Location i and j
		10	14	20	22	30	42	Distance d_{ij}
A–C	135	W 1350	V 1890	W 2700	U 2970	T 4050	S 5670	
C–D	130	1300	1820	2600	W 2860	U 3900	T 5460	
B–C	95	950	1330	1900	V 2090	W 2850	U 3990	
B–D	82	S 820	W 1176	V 1640	T 1804	U 2460	W 3444	
A–B	55	T 550	770	1100	U 1210	W 1750	2310	
A–D	50	U 500	700	1000	W 1100	V 1500	2100	

The minimum optimal solution of the matrix by linear programming will always fall along the main diagonal. However, since by the natural constraints of the equipment location problem a machine can only be in one location, the main diagonal solution is nonfeasible since, for example, the first two cells along the main diagonal requires machines A, C, and D to be located in position 4, 3, and 1 respectively, but when the third cell along the main diagonal is brought into solution B and C must be in locations 2 and 4, but this is not compatible with the earlier assignments and therefore, nonfeasible.

In order to arrive at the optimal feasible solution, it is necessary to start at the northeast corner cell of the load-distance matrix, eliminating the northeast corner location assignments and all other locations dependent upon the northeast corner cell. For example, the northeast corner cell assigns machines A and C to locations 1 and 2 which means machines B

and D cannot be assigned to locations 3 and 4 if the northeast corner cell is eliminated since the two combinations are components of the same solution. These two eliminated cells are marked S in the matrix.

We now move to the minor diagonal lying closest to the northeast corner and eliminate these and all dependent machine location combinations. Those cells eliminated by this diagonal are marked T. For the second minor diagonal the cells eliminated are marked U. For the fourth minor diagonal those cells eliminated in the same manner are marked W.

At this point note that the first and fourth rows and the fourth and fifth columns have only one cell remaining and these must be in the final solution.

It remains necessary to determine compatible locations. Collecting the machine location combinations feasible assignments can be made using the single remaining column and row cells. The combinations are:

$$AC \text{ in } 1\text{–}3$$
$$BD \text{ in } 2\text{–}4$$
$$BC \text{ in } 1\text{–}4$$
$$AD \text{ in } 2\text{–}3$$

which results in the following assignments:

$$A \text{ in location } 3$$
$$B \text{ in location } 4$$
$$C \text{ in location } 1$$
$$D \text{ in location } 2$$

In general, Wimmert's method will result in an optimum solution for n machines in n possible locations. However, the optimality of the solution using successive diagonals starting with the northeast corner does not necessarily hold when a value in a diagonal near the northeast corner is less than a value in a diagonal further from the northeast corner. If this occurs, an optimal or near optimal solution may be obtained by eliminating the high value cell and its dependents before the lower diagonal value. For example, in the example if cell $(B\text{–}C, 1\text{–}4)$ had been 2900 it and its dependents would be eliminated before all cells in the preceding diagonal, except cell $(B\text{–}D, 1\text{–}2)$, which is the only cell on the diagonal with a value in excess of 2900.

Extensions of Wimmert's Method[3]

Wimmert's method can be extended removing the restriction of interchangeable machine areas and by extension of the measurement unit to other than distance-volume.

---

[3] David W. Willoughby, "A Technique for Integrating Facility Location and Materials Handling Equipment Selection" (MSIE thesis, Purdue University, 1967).

To accomplish the first, if area requirements for each function are known, a lowest common denominator of unit area can be determined. For example, if function A requires 50 square feet and function B 100 square feet, the lowest common denominator is 50 square feet with A requiring one unit and B two units. However, it is necessary that B's two units be adjacent. Therefore, any analysis procedure must assure that the area for B be continuous. This can be accomplished by placing a high value on having the unit areas adjacent. This is shown in the example following. Another problem may be present. That is that the shape of the area may be fixed. If considering single machines this may often arise. If considering departments (machine groups or office functions) the shape is usually flexible since the individual work areas (for example, desks in the office) can be efficiently arranged in some variety of shape of total function area. The following procedure will not provide for fixed shapes unless the fixed shape is the unit area.

Wimmert's method does not require effectiveness measure by distance-volume. Rather, any adaptable measurement unit can be used which lends itself to minimization, or in fact, maximization, dependent upon the objective function when using the measurement unit adapted. Now, assume a situation in which areas can be determined but volume is difficult or impossible to measure. However, the proximity advantage of having two functions adjacent can be estimated. (Note that this is often true in the office.) Proximity distance can then be used to assign functions to areas.

We assume an office area 60 x 90 feet to be occupied by an office having four functions A, B, C, and D requiring 1800, 1800, 900, and 900 square feet respectively. The total area can be divided into unit areas of 30 x 30 feet which is the lowest common denominator of required functional areas. This division is shown in Figure 8–1.

FIGURE 8–1

Total Area Divided into Unit Area

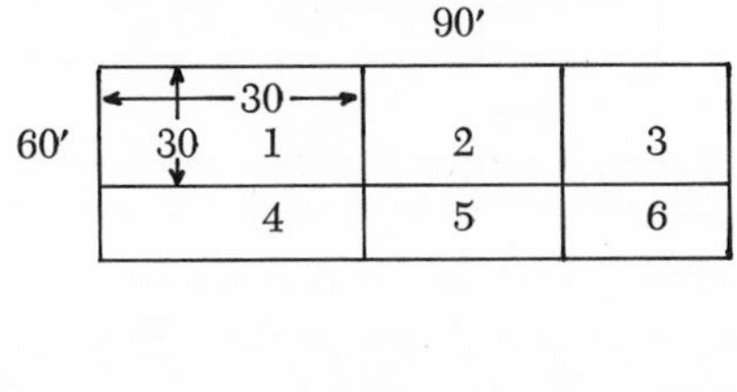

A proximity value is now determined to measure the relative desirability of having functions close to each other. This is done using the following relationship values (values may be established at levels desired):

Proximity Desirability	Point Value
Unit areas of same function	20
Closeness mandatory	5
Frequent contact highly desirable	4
Contact routine but not frequent	3
Contact occurs but not routine	2
Closeness unimportant	1
Undesirable to be close	0

Using the proximity values established a proximity matrix, Table 8–2, may be developed for unit areas. Note that areas A and B have been divided into the unit areas A_1 and A_2 and B_1 and B_2 respectively.

TABLE 8–2

Proximity Matrix

Functions	A_1	A_2	B_1	B_2	C	D
A_1	–	20	3	3	4	1
A_2		–	3	3	4	1
B_1			–	20	5	0
B_2				–	5	0
C					–	2
D						–

The distance matrix is shown in Table 8–3. Distances have been measured area center to area center.

TABLE 8–3

Distance Matrix

Locations	1	2	3	4	5	6
1		30	60	30	42	68
2		–	30	42	30	42
3			–	68	42	30
4				–	30	60
5					–	30
6						–

The decision matrix with nondecreasing columns and nonincreasing rows is shown in Figure 8–2.

An alternative simplified method for reducing the matrix is now illustrated. This reduction technique provides the same results as successive elimination of diagonals and dependents starting with the northeast corner:

1. Prepare a tally matrix in the following manner:
    a) Label column headings with single locations, one column per location.

FIGURE 8–2

Decision Matrix

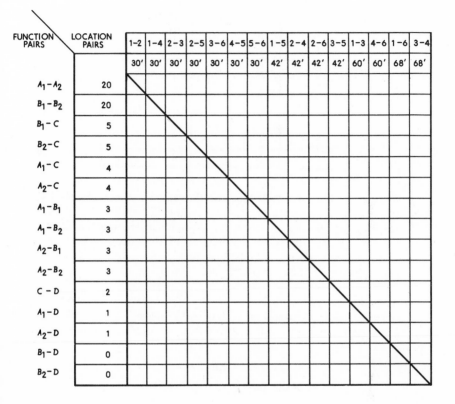

FUNCTION PAIRS	LOCATION PAIRS	1–2	1–4	2–3	2–5	3–6	4–5	5–6	1–5	2–4	2–6	3–5	1–3	4–6	1–6	3–4
		30'	30'	30'	30'	30'	30'	30'	42'	42'	42'	42'	60'	60'	68'	68'
A_1-A_2	20															
B_1-B_2	20															
B_1-C	5															
B_2-C	5															
A_1-C	4															
A_2-C	4															
A_1-B_1	3															
A_1-B_2	3															
A_2-B_1	3															
A_2-B_2	3															
$C-D$	2															
A_1-D	1															
A_2-D	1															
B_1-D	0															
B_2-D	0															

Order is not critical. Leave one additional column labeled "Tallies Required for Elimination."

b) Provide the same number of row headings as on the decision matrix. Then split each row into two rows—using dotted lines—and label each new row with one of the functional pair functions of the corresponding original decision. See Figure 8–3.

c) The number of tally marks required to eliminate a function from a location is equal to the number of original locations (six in the example) minus one minus the number of times the function has appeared as a row heading prior to the row being considered. For example, for the row's pair B_1-C, B_1 has been the row heading once previously and therefore the tally required in this row is $(6-1-1) = 4$. However, this is the first time C has been a row heading and therefore $(6-1) = 5$ tally marks necessary to eliminate a location alternative.

2. On a separate *narrow* strip of paper transpose the row vector of column headings to a column vector (*e.g.*, list vertically the location pairs in non-

FIGURE 8–3

Tally Matrix

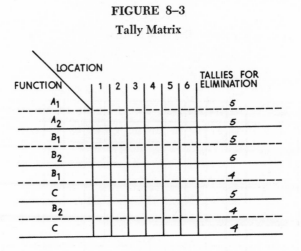

decreasing distance order). Maintain the same line spacing on the location strip as the two-function row spacing on the tally matrix.

3. Align the bottom (largest distance) location pair of the location strip with the top (largest function) combination of the tally matrix. Place tally marks in those cells of the individual function rows in the location column corresponding to the locations aligned with the row headings (see Figure 8–4).

4. Slide the location strip down one paired function row and mark tallies of corresponding locations for both paired functions aligned with locations. Continue moving the location strip down one function pair row at a time.

FIGURE 8–4

Use of the Tally Matrix—First Iteration

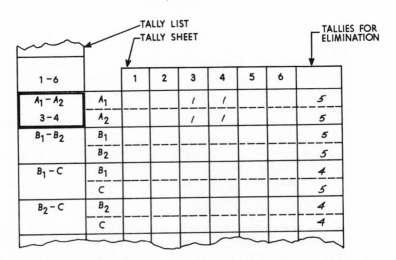

FIGURE 8-5
Use of the Tally Matrix—Fourth Iteration

3-5		1	2	3	4	5	6	TALLIES FOR ELIMINATION
A_1-A_2	A_1	//		//	//		//	5
1-3	A_2	//		//	//		//	5
B_1-B_2	B_1	/		/	//		//	5
4-6	B_2	/		/	//		//	5
B_1-C	B_1	/		/	/		/	4
1-6	C	/		/	/		/	5
B_2 C	B_2			/	/			4
3-4	C			/	/			4

When either member of a function pair has the limiting number of tally marks under a location column, that location is eliminated for that pair (see Figure 8–5 for fourth iteration).

5. Continue until by using the last remaining location pair for function pairs, all function pairs may be assigned to locations (see Figure 8–6 for the final iteration). Note that as a function is assigned to a location that location column is eliminated. Note also that after eliminating column 3, A_2 and B_2 must be assigned to 4 and 6, continuing down to row A_2–D, A_2 must be assigned to location 1 or 6. Since location 6 will satisfy A_2 in each function combination, A_2 is assigned to location 6 thereby fixing B_2 and D.

The above procedures are presented for manual solution. Each may be programmed for solution on a digital computer.

Arrangement by Simulation

Armour and Buffa[4] have derived a simulation algorithm capable of using a digital computer to arrange a plant of up to 40 departments.[5] In order to use the algorithm a preliminary arrangement is established compatible with computer program organization, as well as known departmental area requirements. This is similar to the initial arrangement for travel charting with one significant difference. Each department is com-

---

[4] G. C. Armour, and E. S. Buffa, "A Heuristic Algorithm and Simulation Approach to Relative Location of Facilities," *Management Science,* Vol. 9 (January, 1963), p. 294.

[5] E. S. Buffa, *Models for Production and Operations Management* (New York: John Wiley & Sons, Inc., 1963), pp. 532–538.

FIGURE 8–6

Tally Matrix—Final Iteration

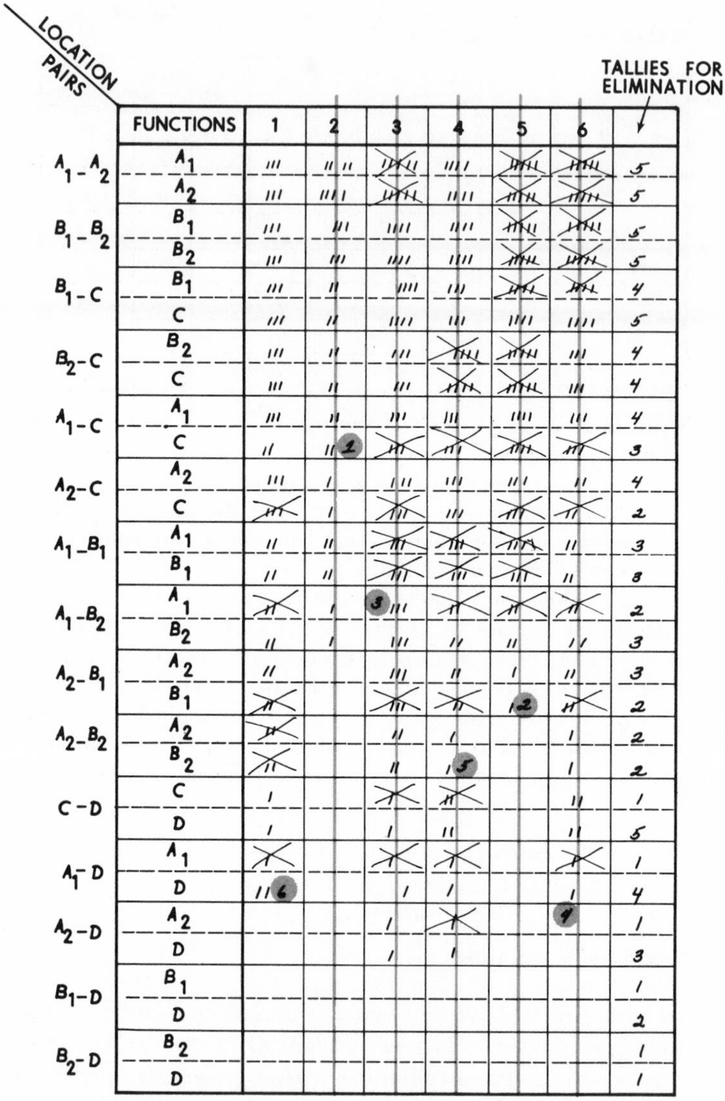

LOCATION PAIRS	FUNCTIONS	1	2	3	4	5	6	TALLIES FOR ELIMINATION
A_1–A_2	A_1	///	// //	//// //	/// /	//// //	//// ////	5
	A_2	///	// / /	//// //	// / /	//// //	//// ////	5
B_1–B_2	B_1	///	///	////	////	//// //	//// ///	5
	B_2	///	///	////	////	//// //	//// ////	5
B_1–C	B_1	///	//	////	///	//// /	//// /	4
	C	///	//	////	///	////	//// /	5
B_2–C	B_2	///	//	///	//// //	//// //	///	4
	C	///	//	///	////	//// //	///	4
A_1–C	A_1	///	//	///	///	////	///	4
	C	//	// **1**	////	///	//// //	////	3
A_2–C	A_2	///	/	/ //	/// /	//// /	// /	4
	C	////	/	////	///	////	////	2
A_1–B_1	A_1	//	//	////	////	////	//	3
	B_1	//	//	////	////	////	//	8
A_1–B_2	A_1	////	/	**3** ///	////	////	////	2
	B_2	//	/	////	//	//	// /	3
A_2–B_1	A_2	//		/// /	//	/	//	3
	B_1	////		////	////	**2** /	////	2
A_2–B_2	A_2	////		//	/		/	2
	B_2	////		//	/ **5**		/	2
C–D	C	/		////	////		//	1
	D	/		/	//		//	5
A_1–D	A_1	////		////	////		////	1
	D	// **6**		/	/		/	4
A_2–D	A_2			/	////		**4**	1
	D			/	/			3
B_1–D	B_1							1
	D							2
B_2–D	B_2							1
	D							1

NOTE: Shaded numbers and lines indicate assignment sequence and location elimina-tions. Elimination locations are X'd. Order assigned: C to 2, B_1 to 5, A_1 to 3, A_2 to 6, B_2 to 4, and D to 1.

posed of one or more unit square areas, which are combined and arranged to provide the department requirement in a contiguous area which is a combination of squares and/or rectangles. This permits the computer program to seek new plant arrangements while retaining total area requirements of each department.

Input into the algorithm in addition to departmental area includes handling volume in unit loads moved between departments and handling cost per unit load per 100 feet between department pairs. These inputs require: (1) that unit loads for all moves be defined, and (2) that unit cost of handling per unit distance be established in advance. This last requires that the handling method between departments be established independent of plant arrangement. This may be dangerous for those seeking a direct analytical solution since experience proves a high level of dependence between handling method and plant arrangement. Second, the assumption of linear correlation between cost and distance handled may introduce error. All things considered, however, if the inherent assumptions of the technique are recognized a good feasible solution is obtained by the algorithm.

The procedure is basically as follows:

1. Determine the area requirements of each department.
2. Determine a common unit square area such that multiples of this unit square can be used to represent departmental areas. A convenient size is 10 feet x 10 feet, permitting departmental areas to be expressed in multiples of unit squares of 100 square feet. For example if there are four departments:

   A of 2400 square feet = 24–10′ x 10′ square
   B of 1600 square feet = 16–10′ x 10′ square
   C of 1100 square feet = 11–10′ x 10′ square
   D of 900 square feet = 9–10′ x 10′ square

3. Determine the load matrix L, *i.e.*:

	A	B	C	D
A		100	40	75
B			160	80
C				90

   $L = [l_{ij}] = $

   where l_{ij} is the number of loads moved between locations i and j per unit time period.

4. Determine the cost matrix C, in which c_{ij} represents the cost of moving one load 100 feet between locations i and j:

	A	B	C	D
A		$0.14	$0.20	$0.14
B			$0.06	$0.18
C				$0.18
D				

   $C = [c_{ij}] = $

Note that in order to determine c_{ij}, the method of handling must be established. Furthermore, a unit cost per unit distance must be established. As we have seen previously, unit cost per unit distance will vary with level of use of equipment. Therefore, if either level of use of selected equipment varies significantly from the level assumed initially or if other methods of handling are to be looked at for movement between two locations a new cost matrix must be established, and the problem re-evaluated.

5. Establish an initial arrangement using combinations of the common unit area for each department. For example, if the above four departments are to be located in a building 60 feet x 100 feet, the following feasible arrangement is established (each letter represents a common unit area (10′ x 10′) of the department identified by the letter):

$$
\begin{array}{cccccccccc}
A & A & A & A & A & C & C & C & C & C \\
A & A & A & A & A & C & C & C & D & D \\
A & A & A & A & A & C & C & C & D & D \\
A & A & A & B & B & B & B & B & D & D \\
A & A & A & B & B & B & B & B & D & D \\
A & A & A & B & B & B & B & B & D & D
\end{array}
$$

A data card is prepared for each row, the card columns representing the proper code letter for the unit area. These cards serve as the digital computer input. The output is printed in the same manner providing a revised arrangement.

6. The digital computer program which has been developed[6] will exchange any departments of equal size or departments which are adjacent but of unequal size. By repeated sequences within the computer program these permit exchange between any departments. The program determines distances between departments in any arrangment and from this, using the handling cost matrix, seeks minimum cost for exchanges of department locations.

7. After finding an exchange which reduces material handling cost the computer prints out the new arrangement, cost, cost reduction, and the departmental exchange from the previous to the new arrangement. This is repeated until no further cost reduction is possible by the program.

The simulation procedure of Armour and Buffa (see Figure 8–7) provides a means of transferring the selection of alternative arrangement to a high speed computer, thereby reducing analysis time and the likelihood of overlooking an improved departmental arrangement. It is necessary, however, to establish handling costs before entering the program. Thereby no allowance is made for interdependencies between arrangement, handling equipment utilization, and handling method selection.

Addition of New Equipment to Existing Layouts

Linear programming and level curve techniques can be used to select the optimum from a number of alternative possible locations of new equipment in an existing layout. The following conditions must be satisfied, however, in order to provide optimum:

---

[6] Gordon C. Armour, "Heuristic Algorithm and Simulation Approach to Relative Location of Facilities" (Unpublished Doctoral dissertation), University of California, Los Angeles, Calif., 1961.

a) Present layout is known.
b) Equipment to be added is known.
c) All possible locations of the new equipment are known.
d) Activity levels between existing and new equipment combinations are known.
e) Costs of handling are known. Note, these are usually assumed linear to the distance-volume of a move in the layout.

FIGURE 8–7

**Elementary Block Diagram for Armour-Buffa
Simulation**

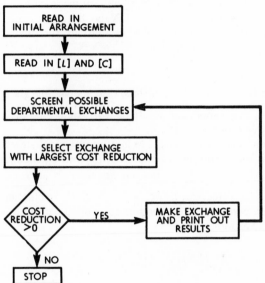

Level curves. Level curves may be used to locate a new machine in an existing facility. The primary logic is to develop isocost curves between existing and the new equipment, then selecting the alternative available location for the new equipment which lies upon the lowest isocost curve. We look at some type cases:

1. One machine to be located relative to one other machine.
    If E is an existing machine then the isocost curves are concentric circles having E as their common center. The new equipment should be located on the intermost possible isocost curve, or the minimum distance from E.
2. One machine to be located relative to two existing machines.
    If E_1 and E_2 are two existing machines the minimum cost is obtained when the new equipment is located on the line connecting E_1 and E_2. If the volume (cost) of handling is equal between the new machine and each of the existing machines cost is minimized by locating at any point between

E_1 and E_2. If the volumes differ and cost is assumed linear to the distance-volume product, minimum cost is obtained when $v_1d_1 = v_2d_2$.

Where the ratio $\dfrac{d_1}{d_2} = \dfrac{v_2}{v_1}$ and $(d_1 + d_2) =$ the linear distance between

E_1 and $E_2 = D$. Therefore, $d_1 = (D - d_1)\dfrac{v_2}{v_1}$, or

$$d_1 = \frac{D}{1 + \left(\dfrac{v_1}{v_2}\right)}, \text{and } d_2 = D - d_1.$$

3. One work station to be located relative to n, existing work stations with straight-line (conveyor) handling between work stations. Let $E_1, E_2 \ldots$ E_k be existing work stations and N be the new work station. Then a handling volume vector V can be established, such that v_k is the volume moved between N and E_k, e.g.:

$$V = v_1, v_2 \ldots, v_k,$$

Then for any location of N_{ij} the total distance-volume (cost) is $\displaystyle\sum_k$ (distance (ij) to E_k) v_k location, and locations with equal total distance-volume can be considered isocost locations.

For example, assume we are to locate a new machine which has common flow with three existing machines, E_1, E_2, and E_3 such that

$$V = 20, 40, 30$$

and the plant area can be represented as a combination of square unit areas each with centers ij, therefore forming a matrix L_{ij}, with E_1, E_2, and E_3 located as indicated.

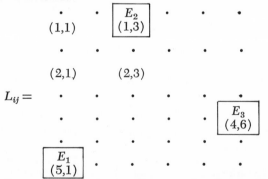

Then the distance-volume matrix, wherein each cell unit value, of equivalent cost,

$$c_{ij} = \sum_k \text{distance } (l_{ij} \text{ to } E_k) v_k$$

For example:

$$c_{11} = 4(20) + 2(40) + \sqrt{3^2 + 5^2}(30)$$
$$c_{21} = 3(V_o) + \sqrt{2^2 + 1^2}(40) + \sqrt{2^2 + 5^2}(30)$$

Continuing in like manner results in the following cost matrix:

$$C_{ij} = \begin{matrix} 337 & 272 & \times & 248 & 288 & 338 \\ 310 & 255 & 220 & 224 & 268 & 306 \\ 305 & 267 & 232 & 240 & 244 & 282 \\ 314 & 276 & 258 & 252 & 256 & \times \\ \times & 309 & 296 & 296 & 302 & 330 \end{matrix}$$

The cost matrix results in location (2,3) having minimum cost of 220 measured in distance-volume.

ASSIGNMENT MODEL LINEAR PROGRAMMING

The assignment model is a special case of the distribution or transportation problem in linear programming identified by unity rim conditions. In general, there are n resources to assign to n users and the assignments are in such a manner that all of a resource i is assigned to a user j or none of the resource i is assigned to j. This condition results in an n by n matrix representation, the solution of which results in each resource being assigned to one and only one user in such a manner that the total cost of assignment is minimized.

In general the assignment problem can be defined as: Given an n^2 cost matrix $C = (c_{ij})$ with $c_{ij} \geq 0$ for $i, j = 1, 2, 3, \ldots, n$ find an n^2 solution matrix $S = (s_{ij})$ such that:

$$\sum_{i=1}^{n} (s_{ij}) \sum_{j=1}^{n} (s_{ij}) = 1$$

where $s^2_{ij} = s_{ij}$ and total cost $= TC = \sum c_{ij}s_{ij}$ is a minimum.

It also holds that if from the cost matrix $C = (c_{ij})$ we form another matrix $X = (x_{ij})$ where $x_{ij} = c_{ij} - u_i - v_j$, and where u_i and v_j are constants the solution of the cost matrix C is the same as cost matrix X. We now adapt this to the machine location problem.

As we have seen cost of handling is dependent upon a number of variables including handling method and equipment and labor utilization which makes the assignment of a dollar cost for movement difficult. If, however, we assume handling between all operations under consideration will be by an identical handling method then the total cost of handling in the system will approach a direct relationship to the sum of the distance-volume products of individual paths between locations. By this assumption distance-volume products may represent cell costs (x_{ij}) in the C matrix. In like manner we can assume locations as resources and machines as users or customers and if the number of machines equals the number of interchangeable locations which can be assigned to any one of the machines we can establish the n^2 cost matrix to which the assignment problem solution can be applied. In summary the critical assumptions and conditions are:

1. Given n machines to assign to.
2. n interchangeable locations.
3. Cost can be represented by distance-volume of handling items.
4. Handling occurs only between new machines and existing machines with no movement between combinations of the new machines.

Under the above conditions we now solve the following example using the assignment model. Given four new machines A, B, C, and D interacting with three existing machines I, II, and III so that the total loads between machines can be represented by the following load matrix L:

		I	II	III
	A	65	135	60
$L = l_{ij} =$	B	70	95	82
	C	105	0	130
	D	90	30	45

There are four interchangeable available locations 1, 2, 3, 4 with distance relationships to existing machines as represented in the distance matrix D:

		1	2	3	4
	I	42	14	22	50
$D = d_{jk} =$	II	20	30	20	36
	III	72	60	10	20

We now find the product matrix $P = LD$:

		1	2	3	4
	A	9450	8565	4730	9310
$P = B$	B	10744	8750	4250	8060
	C	13770	9270	3610	7850
	D	7620	4860	3030	6480

Solving by the assignment rule:

1. Reduce the entries of each row by the minimum value in that row.

	1	2	3	4
A	4620	3835	0	4580
B	6494	4500	0	3810
C	10160	5660	0	4240
D	4590	1830	0	3450

2. Repeat step 1 for columns

	1	2	3	4
A	30	2005	0	1130
B	1904	2670	0	360
C	5570	3830	0	790
D	0	0	0	0

3. Select the smallest cell value after step 2 which does not lie on one of the minimum number of lines drawn through zeros, e.g., 30. Subtract this value from all cell values not on a "zero line" and add it to zero line intersections.

	1	2	3	4
A	0	1975	0	1100
B	1874	2640	0	330
C	5540	3800	0	760
D	0	0	30	0

4. Repeat step 3 until zero lines $= n$.

	1	2	3	4
A	0	1975	330	1100
B	1544	2310	0	0
C	5210	3470	0	430
D	0	0	360	0

Since zero lines $= 4 = n$, the assignment is solved:

$$\text{Solution} = P_{11} + P_{24} + P_{33} + P_{42}$$

and the optimum assignments are:

Machine A to location 1
Machine B to location 4
Machine C to location 3
Machine D to location 2

which from the P matrix results in a minimum load distance of 25,980.

A DYNAMIC PROGRAMMING TECHNIQUE FOR SOLVING THE JOINT FACILITY LOCATION–HANDLING SYSTEM SELECTION PROBLEM[7]: LACH[7a]

Using the dynamic programming strategy to solve the facility location handling system selection problem requires that it first be recognized that it can be structured as a multistage, sequential decision problem. The problem is to assign n facilities to m locations, where $m \geq n$. (These facilities are analogous to the stages of a multistage process.) Each materials handling flow path is also treated as a stage in the structure.

If the location handling system selection problem is structured for dynamic programming solution in the normal manner, treating each facility and flow path as separate stages results in an unmanageable number of inputs at the latter stages, for a reasonable problem. This can be avoided by structuring the problem as a two-directional problem.

Consider a single facility which is to be assigned to one of the available locations which can accommodate it. Goods must be transported between this facility and other facilities, either new or existing. Each of these materials handling relationships or flow paths will be considered a stage in dynamic programming as shown in Figure 8–8. The state variables speci-

---

[7] Adapted from Willoughby, *op. cit.*
[7a] Location Assignment by Cost of Handling.

FIGURE 8-8

Dynamic Programming Model for a Single Facility

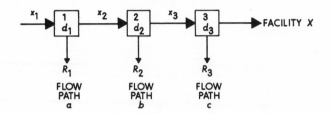

fying each of these stages can be characterized as follows:

1. Inputs to each stage contain two pieces of information or parameters. These are alternative locations for the facility being considered and the total amount of money "spent" for the purchase of materials handling equipment at previous stages.
2. The set of decisions at each stage depict the alternative materials handling systems under consideration for transporting goods over the given flow path.
3. The outputs from each stage transmit two pieces of information to subsequent stages; namely, the locations available for occupancy by other facilities at subsequent stages and the total amount of money "spent" for the purchase of materials handling equipment, including equipment selected at the present stage.
4. Returns at each stage reflect the materials handling costs incurred for each of the various decisions and stage inputs. The cost per unit time of transporting goods between facilities i and j by means of materials handling system k is calculated as:

$$E = v_{ij}{}^{(k)} \, d_{ij}{}^{(k)} \, c_{ij}{}^{(k)}$$

Using these state variables, dynamic programming can be employed to select materials handling systems for each flow path such that the cost to connect the given facility with every other facility is minimized for each possible input (facility location). Similar analysis can be performed for each new facility. Dynamic programming can then be applied across facilities, in the vertical direction shown by the double arrow in Figure 8-9 which spans all facilities, to assign facilities to locations and materials handling systems to flow paths such that total materials handling costs are minimized subject to capital budgeting constraints.

Because of the budget constraint, the order in which the facilities and flow paths are considered determines the inputs, allowable decisions, outputs and returns at each stage. For this reason, it seems logical that facilities and flow paths be considered in decreasing order of total materials handling volume. Treating the higher volume facilities first assures that funds will be available to purchase specialized equipment to handle the heavier interfacility flows.

FIGURE 8-9

Dynamic Programming Model for Three Facilities

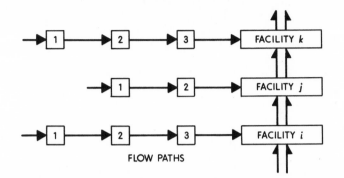

This strategy to solve the facility location-handling system selection problem by dynamic programming can be summarized as follows:

1. Determine the total materials handling volume in unit loads to flow between each new facility and every other facility, new or existing.
2. Treat the facility having the highest total volume as the first stage of the problem.
3. Using dynamic programming in the horizontal direction (across flow paths for the first considered facility), as shown in Figure 8-9, select materials handling systems for each flow path so that the cost to connect the given facility with every other facility is minimized for each possible input (location).
4. Bringing forward only the optimal outputs from stage (facility) 1, perform similar analysis for the second facility, and so on, for all facilities.
5. Using dynamic programming in the vertical direction as shown in Figure 8-9, assign facilities to locations and materials handling systems to flow paths so that total materials handling costs are minimized.

APPLICATION OF LACH
TO A SAMPLE FACILITY LOCATION–HANDLING SYSTEM
SELECTION PROBLEM

Statement of the Problem

Suppose we wish to locate three new facilities on a plant floor. Four existing facilities are already in operation in the plant and their materials handling loading and unloading stations are designated as F_I, F_{II}, F_{III}, and F_{IV} as in Figure 8–10.

There are four locations on the plant floor which may accommodate one or more of the new facilities. These locations are designated by Arabic numerals in Figure 8–10. (Points in the layout area are located as coordinates of a Cartesian plane whose axes intersect at the southwest corner of the layout area.)

Plant Location, Layout, and Maintenance

FIGURE 8-10

Location of Existing Facilities
and Available Areas in the
Sample Problem

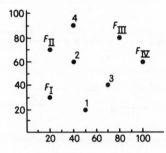

Facilities to be located are limited to the available locations as shown in Table 8-4.

TABLE 8-4

Acceptable Locations for the New Facilities

Available Locations

New Facilities	L_1	L_2	L_3	L_4
A	✔	X	✔	X
B	X	✔	✔	✔
C	✔	✔	✔	✔

(A check mark (✔) in the table means that the new facility may be assigned to that location and an (X) indicates that the location cannot accommodate the facility.)

Suppose there are five materials handling systems being considered to handle the required materials handling flow between the new and existing facilities. The five systems, their purchase price and operation costs are:

System	Purchase Price	Operation Cost
P = Fork truck	$5000 each	$0.016 per unit load-foot
Q = Hand truck	$ 300 each	$0.012 per unit load-foot
R = Low-lift electric hand truck	$2000 each	$0.018 per unit load-foot
S = Belt conveyor	$25 per lineal foot	$0.010 per ton-foot
T = Trolley conveyor	$40 per lineal foot	$0.012 per ton-foot

Operation cost contains capital recovery, operating, and maintenance cost elements.

The equivalent distance in feet between available locations and existing facilities by means of the respective materials handling systems are shown in Table 8–5. Again, Roman numerals designate existing facilities and Arabic numbers designate available locations.

TABLE 8–5

Equivalent Distance in Feet between Available Locations and Existing Facilities for Various Materials Handling Systems

Location Pairs	Handling Systems				
	P	Q	R	S	T
1–2	60	60	55	41	44
1–3	55	45	45	28	31
1–4	95	90	90	71	74
2–3	55	50	50	36	39
2–4	40	30	30	30	33
3–4	95	90	90	58	61
I–1	50	50	50	41	44
I–2	65	60	60	36	39
I–3	75	70	75	51	54
I–4	95	85	95	63	66
II–1	95	85	85	58	61
II–2	40	40	40	22	25
II–3	95	85	95	58	61
II–4	55	60	50	28	31
III–1	105	105	100	67	70
III–2	75	70	70	45	48
III–3	65	60	65	41	44
III–4	60	60	60	41	44
IV–1	105	105	100	64	67
IV–2	70	70	70	60	63
IV–3	65	60	65	28	31
IV–4	105	100	100	67	70

Table 8–6 shows the alternative materials handling systems being considered to transport goods between the facilities.

TABLE 8–6

Materials Handling Alternatives between the Respective Facilities

	A	B	C	F_I	F_{II}	F_{III}	F_{IV}
A	...	P, R, T	Q, R, S	P	P, T	Q, R, T	X
B	...	...	X	Q, S	X	X	Q, S
C	...	...	...	X	P, R	X	Q, R

The materials handling volume in tons per month flowing between facilities is shown in Table 8–7.

TABLE 8–7

Materials Handling Volumes between the Respective Facilities
in Tons per Month

	A	B	C	F_I	F_{II}	F_{III}	F_{IV}
A	...	300	200	250	150	450	X
B	...	...	X	100	X	X	50
C	...	...	...	X	400	X	250

The materials handling volume in unit loads per month flowing between the facilities is shown in Table 8–8.

TABLE 8–8

Materials Handling Volume in Unit Loads per Month between Facilities

	$A\text{–}B$	$A\text{–}C$	$F_I\text{–}A$	$F_I\text{–}B$	$F_{II}\text{–}A$	$F_{II}\text{–}C$	$F_{III}\text{–}A$	$F_{IV}\text{–}B$	$F_{IV}\text{–}C$
P	150	X	125	X	75	200	X	X	X
Q	X	800	X	400	X	X	1800	X	1000
R	300	200	X	X	X	400	450	50	250
S	X	200	X	100	X	X	X	50	X
T	300	X	X	X	150	X	450	X	X

Finally, due to capital restraints, no more than \$17,000 may be spent on materials handling equipment.

From Table 8–7: new facility A exchanges the most goods with the other facilities, 1350 tons; facility C is second; and facility B exchanges the least goods with other facilities. The new facilities will therefore be treated in the order A, C, B.

From Table 8–6, facility A exchanges goods with fixed facilities F_I, F_{II}, and F_{III}, which represents three stages for facility A. The inputs, decisions, and outputs for these stages can be summarized in the three-part tableau of Table 8–9.

TABLE 8–9

Investment Cost Tableau for Facility A Flow Paths

Stage 1
Flow Path $A\text{–}F_{III}$

x_1	d_1		
	Q	R	T
L_1	$L_{2,3,4}$ 1200	$L_{2,3,4}$ 2000	$L_{2,3,4}$ 2800
L_3	$L_{1,2,4}$ 900	$L_{1,2,4}$ 2000	$L_{1,2,4}$ 1760

Stage 2
Flow Path
$A\text{–}F_I$

x_2	d_2
	P
L_1	$L_{2,3,4}$ 5000
L_3	$L_{1,2,4}$ 5000

Stage 3
Flow Path $A\text{–}F_{II}$

x_3	d_3	
	P	T
L_1	$L_{2,3,4}$ 5000	$L_{2,3,4}$ 2440
L_3	$L_{1,2,4}$ 5000	$L_{1,2,4}$ 2440

The tableau for stage 1 shows that if facility A is assigned to location three (L_3) and a trolley conveyor is used to transport goods from new facility A to existing facility F_{III}, then locations L_1, L_2, and L_4 will be available for occupancy by facilities C and B and \$1760 must be spent to install the trolley conveyor.

The cost of the trolley conveyor to connect facilities A and F_{III} was calculated as follows:

Purchase price of trolley conveyor   = \$ 40 per foot
Equivalent distance between F_{III} and
   L_3 by means of trolley conveyor   =   44 feet
     Total cost = 44 feet (\$40/foot) = \$1760.

The monthly materials handling cost, resulting from each input and decision at these respective stages, is summarized in Table 8–10.

TABLE 8–10

Operating Cost Tableau for Facility A Flow Paths

	Stage 1 Flow Path A–F_{III}			Stage 2 Flow Path A–F_I		Stage 3 Flow Path A–F_{II}	
	d_1			d_2		d_3	
x_1	Q	R	T	x_2	P	x_3	P	T
L_1	2270	810	378	L_1	100	L_1	114	110
L_3	1300	527	238	L_3	150	L_3	114	110

The stage 1 tableau of Table 8–10 reveals that if facility A is assigned to location three (L_3) and a trolley conveyor is used to transport goods between facilities A and F_{III}, a materials handling cost of \$238 per month will be incurred.

The monthly cost to transport goods between facility A and F_{III} by means of a trolley conveyor was calculated in the following manner:

Operating cost for trolley conveyor   = \$0.012 per ton-foot
Volume of goods flowing between
   facilities A and F_{III} =   450 tons per month
Equivalent distance between facilities A and
   F_{III} by means of a trolley conveyor   =   44 feet
(44 feet) (450 tons/month) (0.012/ton-feet) = \$ 238 per month
   Total materials handling cost   = \$ 238 per month.

From the information contained in these investment and operating three-part tableaus, the optimal decision for each flow path and input can be determined and summarized into decision tableau as shown in Table 8–11.

TABLE 8–11

Decision Tableau for Facility A Flow Paths

Stage 1 Flow Path $A–F_{III}$				Stage 2 Flow Path $A–F_I$				Stage 3 Flow Path $A–F_{II}$			
x_1	d_1'	X_2	f_1'	x_2	d_2'	X_2	f_2'	x_3	d_3'	X_2	f_3'
L_1	T	$L_{2,3,4}$ 2800	378	L_1	P	$L_{2,3,4}$ 5000	100	L_1	T	$L_{2,3,4}$ 2400	110
L_3	T	$L_{1,2,4}$ 1760	238	L_3	P	$L_{1,2,4}$ 5000	150	L_3	T	$L_{2,3,4}$ 2440	110

In Table 8–11, the column labels are defined as follows:

x_i = The inputs to stage i
d_1' = The optimal decision at stage i for each input
f_1' = The return at stage i for a given input and optimal decision
X_2 = The input to the next stage, or facility C, when dynamic programming in the vertical direction is performed.

The decision tableau for stage 1 (flow path $A–F_{III}$) shows that if facility A is assigned to location three (L_3), a trolley conveyor should be used to transport goods between facilities A and F_{III} (in preference to hand trucks or a low-lift electric hand truck) in order to minimize materials handling costs.

Finally, the information contained in the three-part decision tableau of Table 8–11 can be used to determine an optimal policy concerning facility A for each alternative location. This optimal policy is depicted in Table 8–12.

TABLE 8–12

Decision Table for Facility A

X_1	D_1^*	X_2^*	F_1^*	
L_1	T, P, T	$L_{2,3,4}$ 10240	588	◄
L_3	T, P, T	$L_{1,2,4}$ 9200	498	

In Table 8–12, X_1, D_1^*, X_2^*, and F_1^* are respectively the inputs, optimal decisions, outputs, and optimal returns for facility A, the first stage for dynamic programming in the vertical direction. This decision table states that if facility A is assigned to location three (L_3), the following is true:

    1. A trolley conveyor (T) should be assigned to flow path A-F_{III}, a fork lift truck (P) should be used to transport goods over flow path A-F_I, and a trolley conveyor is also the most economical means of transporting goods between new facility A and existing facility F_{II}.

2. The optimal input to stage 2 for dynamic programming in the vertical direction consists of locations one, two, and four ($L_{1,2,4}$) and the amount of money spent connecting facility A to facilities F_I, F_{II} and F_{III}, \$9200.
3. The monthly cost of this optimal policy concerning facility A, F_I, is \$498.

Having determined the optimal policy for facility A, facility C can now be treated. The inputs, decision sets, and resulting outputs for all three stages for dynamic programming in the horizontal direction are summarized in Table 8–13.

TABLE 8–13

Investment Cost Tableau for Facility C Flow Paths

Stage groups: Stage 1 C–F_{II} Decision (d_1); Stage 2 C–F_{IV} Decision (d_2); Stage 3 C–A Decision (d_3).

Input (X_2) A in	C in	d_1	R	d_2 Q	R	d_3 Q	R	S
L_1 10,240	L_2	$L_{3,4}$ 0	$L_{3,4}$ 2000	$L_{3,4}$ 600	$L_{3,4}$ 2000	$L_{3,4}$ 300	$L_{3,4}$ 2000	$L_{3,4}$ 1025
	L_3	$L_{2,4}$ 0	$L_{2,4}$ 2000	$L_{2,4}$ 600	$L_{2,4}$ 2000	$L_{2,4}$ 300	$L_{2,4}$ 2000	$L_{2,4}$ 700
	L_4	$L_{2,3}$ 0	$L_{2,3}$ 2000	$L_{2,3}$ 600	$L_{2,3}$ 2000	$L_{2,3}$ 600	$L_{2,3}$ 2000	$L_{2,3}$ 1775
L_3 9200	L_1	$L_{2,4}$ 0	$L_{2,4}$ 2000	$L_{2,4}$ 600	$L_{2,4}$ 2000	$L_{2,4}$ 300	$L_{2,4}$ 2000	$L_{2,4}$ 700
	L_2	$L_{1,4}$ 0	$L_{1,4}$ 2000	$L_{1,4}$ 600	$L_{1,4}$ 2000	$L_{1,4}$ 300	$L_{1,4}$ 2000	$L_{1,4}$ 900
	L_4	$L_{1,2}$ 2000		$L_{1,2}$ 600	$L_{1,2}$ 2000	$L_{1,2}$ 600	$L_{1,2}$ 2000	$L_{1,2}$ 1450

Table 8–13 requires some clarification. First, no capital investment is required to employ a fork truck over flow path C–F_{III} since purchasing a fork truck was part of the optimal policy for facility A. Transporting goods over both flow paths by the same fork truck results in a machine fraction of only 0.0906, using the equation

$$N = \frac{TP}{60HC}$$

where

N = Number of machines (fork trucks) required
T = Standard time per move
P = Number of moves per month
H = Standard hours/month
C = Machine utilization factor, assumed to be 0.70.

The number of hand trucks required for each respective flow path was determined in the same manner.

The costs resulting from each decision, input, and flow path for facility C are shown in Table 8–14.

TABLE 8–14

Operating Cost Tableau for Facility C Flow Paths

Input (X_2)		Stage 1 $C–F_{II}$ Decision (d_1)		Stage 2 $C–F_{IV}$ Decision (d_2)		Stage 3 $C–A$ Decision (d_3)		
A in	C in	P	R	Q	R	Q	R	S
L_1 10,240	L_2	128	288	890	315	576	176	82
	L_3	304	683	720	293	432	144	56
	L_4	176	359	1200	450	864	288	142
L_3 9200	L_1	304	612	1260	450	432	144	56
	L_2	128	288	840	315	480	160	72
	L_4	176	359	1200	450	864	288	116

Table 8–15 indicates the optimal decision at each stage for the various inputs.

TABLE 8–15

Decision Tableau for Facility C Flow Paths

Input (X_2)		Stage 1 $C–F_{II}$		Stage 2 $C–F_{IV}$		Stage 3 $C–A$		
A in	C in	d_1'	f_1'	d_2'	f_2'	d_3'	f_3'	X_3
L_1 10,240	L_2	P	128	R	315	S	82	$L_{3,4}$ 1025
	L_3	P	304	R	293	S	56	$L_{2,4}$ 790
	L_4	P	176	R	450	S	142	$L_{1,4}$ 1775
L_3 9200	L_1	P	304	R	450	S	56	$L_{2,4}$ 700
	L_2	P	128	R	315	S	72	$L_{1,4}$ 900
	L_4	P	176	R	450	S	116	$L_{1,2}$ 1450

The information contained in Table 8–15 can be used to determine the optimal policy concerning facility C. Table 8–16 summarizes this optimal policy.

TABLE 8-16

Decision Table for Facility C

Input (X_2)		$D_2{}^*$	$X_3{}^*$	$F_2{}^*$
A in	*C in*			
L_1 \$10,240	L_2	P, R, S	$L_{3,4}$ 13,265	1113 ◄——
	L_3	P, R, S	$L_{2,4}$ 12,940	1241
	L_4	P, R, S	$L_{2,3}$ 14,015	1356
L_3 9200	L_1	P, R, S	$L_{2,4}$ 11,860	1308
	L_2	P, R, S	$L_{1,4}$ 12,060	1013
	L_4	P, R, S	$L_{1,2}$ 12,610	1240

Having determined the optimal policy concerning facilities A and C, facility B can now be considered. The investment tableaus for flow paths $B-F_I$, $B-F_{IV}$ and $B-A$ are presented as Table 8–17.

TABLE 8-17

Investment Cost Tableau for Facility B Flow Paths

			Stage 1 B–A			Stage 2 B–F_I		Stage 3 B–F_{IV}	
Input (X_3)			Decision			Decision		Decision	
A in	*C in*	*B in*	P	R	T	Q	S	R	S
L_1 \$13,265	L_2	L_3	L_4–0	L_4–0	L_4–1240	L_4–300	L_4–1275	L_4–0	L_4–700
	L_4		L_3–0	L_3–0	L_3–2960	L_3–300	L_3–1575	L_3–0	L_3–1675
L_1 12,940	L_3	L_2	L_4–0	L_4–0	L_4–1800	L_4–300	L_4–900	L_4–0	L_4–1500
	L_4		L_2–0	L_2–0	L_2–2960	L_2–300	L_2–1575	L_2–0	L_2–1675
L_1 14,015	L_4	L_2	L_3–0	L_3–0	L_3–1800	L_3–300	L_3–900	L_3–0	L_3–1500
	L_3		L_2–0	L_2–0	L_2–1240	L_2–300	L_2–1275	L_2–0	L_2–700
L_3 11,860	L_1	L_2	L_4–0	L_4–0	L_4–1560	L_4–300	L_4–900	L_4–0	L_4–1500
	L_4		L_2–0	L_2–0	L_2–2440	L_2–300	L_2–1575	L_2–0	L_2–1675
L_3 12,060	L_2	L_1	X	X	X	X	X	X	X
	L_4		L_1–0	L_1–0	L_1–2440	L_1–300	L_1–1575	L_1–0	L_1–1675
L_3 12,610	L_4	L_1	X	X	X	X	X	X	X
	L_2		L_1–0	L_1–0	L_1–1560	L_1–300	L_1–900	L_1–0	L_1–1500

The monthly cost incurred as a result of alternative decisions for each input and flow path is shown in Table 8–18.

TABLE 8–18

Operating Cost Tableau for Facility B Flow Paths

			Stage 1 B–A			Stage 2 $B–F_I$		Stage 3 $B–F_{IV}$	
Input (X_3)			Decision			Decision		Decision	
A in	C in	B in	P	R	T	Q	S	R	S
L_1	L_2	L_3	132	243	112	336	51	58	14
$13,265		L_4	228	486	256	408	62	90	34
L_1	L_3	L_2	144	297	162	288	36	63	30
12,940		L_4	228	486	256	408	63	90	34
L_1	L_4	L_2	144	297	162	288	36	63	30
14,015		L_3	132	243	112	336	51	58	14
L_3	L_1	L_2	156	270	137	288	36	63	30
11,860		L_4	228	486	220	408	63	90	34
L_3	L_2	L_1	X	X	X	X	X	X	X
12,060		L_4	228	486	220	408	63	90	34
L_3	L_4	L_1	X	X	X	X	X	X	X
12,610		L_3	156	270	137	288	36	63	30

From the information summarized in the facility B investment and operating three-part tableau, a decision table, Table 8–19, can be constructed summarizing the optimal decision for each facility B flow path and input.

TABLE 8–19

Decision Tableau for Facility B Flow Paths

			Stage 1 B–A		Stage 2 $B–F_I$		Stage 3 $B–F_{IV}$	
Input (X_3)								
A in	C in	B in	d_3'	f_3'	d_1'	f_1'	d_2'	f_2'
L_1	L_2	L_3	T	112	S	51	S	14
$11,265		L_4	P	228	S	63	S	34
L_1	L_3	L_2	P	144	S	36	S	30
10,940		L_4	P	228	S	63	S	34
L_1	L_4	L_2	P	144	S	36	S	30
12,015		L_3	T	112	S	51	S	14
L_3	L_1	L_2	T	137	S	36	S	30
9860		L_4	T	220	S	63	S	34
L_3	L_2	L_1	X	X	X	X	X	X
10,060		L_4	T	220	S	63	S	34
L_3	L_4	L_1	X	X	X	X	X	X
10,610		L_2	T	137	S	36	S	30

Finally, the optimal policy concerning facility B can be determined. This optimal policy is depicted in Table 8–20.

TABLE 8–20

Decision Table for Facility *B*

Policy	Input (X_3)			D_3^*	F_3^*	X_4^*	
	A in	*C in*	*B in*				
1	L_1	L_2	L_3	T, S, S	1290	L_4–16,480	◄—
2	\$11,265		L_4	P, S, S	1438	L_3–16,515	
3	L_1	L_3	L_2	P, S, S	1451	L_4–15,340	
4	10,940		L_4	P, S, S	1566	L_2–16,190	
5	L_1	L_4	L_2	P, S, S	1566	L_3–16,415	
6	12,015		L_3	T, S, S	1533	L_4–17,230	
7	L_3	L_1	L_2	T, S, S	1511	L_4–15,860	
8	9860		L_4	T, S, S	1625	L_2–17,590	
9	L_3	L_2	L_1	X	X	X	
10	10,060		L_4	T, S, S	1330	L_1–17,790	
11	L_3	L_4	L_1	X	X	X	
12	10,610		L_3	T, S, S	1443	L_1–16,610	

By scanning the decision table for facility *B*, and applying dynamic programming in the vertical direction, we can determine the overall optimum policy for each facility and flow path in order to minimize total materials handling costs. This overall optimum policy is summarized in Table 8–21, and pointed out by arrows in Tables 8–12, 8–16, and 8–20.

TABLE 8–21

Overall Optimum Facility Location Handling System Selection Policy

	Assigned Location	Flow Path	System Selected	Monthly Cost	Capital Cost
		A–F_{III}	T	\$ 100	\$ 2800
A	L_1	A–F_I	P	110	5000
		A–F_{II}	T	328	2440
		C–F_{II}	P	128	0
C	L_2	C–F_{IV}	R	315	2000
		C–A	S	82	1025
		B–A	T	51	1240
B	L_3	B–F_I	S	14	1275
		B–F_{IV}	S	112	700
Total				\$1290	\$16,480

The dynamic programming technique is an efficient method of solving an otherwise computationally infeasible problem. If it were attempted to solve even the small problem treated by complete enumeration, 20,736 possibilities would have to be investigated. Solution by means of dynamic programming in two directions involved evaluating a total of 222 alternatives for all stages. Even straightforward application of dynamic programming would have resulted in 864 inputs to the final stage, whereas only 12 inputs were involved using the strategy in Table 8–20.

It must be emphasized that the obtained solution is optimal only with respect to the criterion of materials handling cost minimization. It is not professed that this is always the best decision criterion for solution of the location handling system selection problem. In fact, in some cases it is obviously a poor criterion. For instance, in the analysis of facility A, it was determined that a trolley conveyor should be employed to transport goods over flow path A–F_{II}. The purchase price of this conveyor is $2400. However, a fork lift truck could be used to transport goods between facilities A and F_{II} for $114 per month. (See Tables 8–9 and 8–10.) Since a fork lift truck must be purchased for flow path A–F_I, the expenditure of $2400 could be eliminated by using the same truck to transport goods between facilities A and F_{II}. Such considerations indicate that perhaps some measure of the return on money invested would be a more realistic decision criterion than minimization of cost.

MAXIMIZING RATE OF RETURN BY DYNAMIC PROGRAMMING

Capital expenditures usually are authorized only after some type of investment analysis has been performed. Frequently, the relative worth of alternative investments is specified as the rate of return on invested capital.

Rate of return is the interest rate at which the present worth of future receipts and disbursements is equal. To use rate of return as the decision criterion in the solution of the location handling system selection problem, investment alternatives must be compared for each flow path (state) of each new facility. The materials handling system yielding the highest rate of return for each flow path and possible location can be determined for each new facility by dynamic programming in the horizontal direction. Using these optimal results, the overall optimum investment policy for all new facilities can then be determined by dynamic programming in the vertical direction.

The problem solved by cost minimization in the previous section was also solved using maximum rate of return as the decision criterion. Useful life of all equipment was assumed to be six years in this analysis. The decision tables for facilities A, C, and B are shown in Tables 8–22, 8–23, and 8–24, respectively.

TABLE 8–22

Decision Table for Facility A Using Maximum
Rate of Return as the Decision Criterion

X_1	$D_1{}^*$	$X_2{}^*$	F_1
L_1	R, P, P	$L_{2,3,4}$ 7000	1024
L_3	T, P, P	$L_{1,2,4}$ 6760	502 ←

TABLE 8-23

Decision Table for Facility C Using Maximum Rate of Return as the Decision Criterion

Input (X_2)		D_2	X_3	F_2
A in	C in			
L_1	L_2	P, R, R	$L_{3,4}$ 7000	1643
	L_3	P, R, R	$L_{2,4}$ 7000	1765
	L_4	P, R, R	$L_{2,3}$ 7000	1938
L_3	C_1	P, R, R	$L_{2,4}$ 8760	1400
	C_2	P, R, R	L_1 8760	1105 ◀—
	C_4	P, R, R	$L_{1,2}$ 8760	1416

TABLE 8-24

Decision Table for Facility B Using Maximum Rate of Return as the Decision Criterion

Policy	Input (X_3)			$D_3{}^*$	$X_4{}^*$	$F_3{}^*$
	A in	C in	B in			
1	L_1	L_2	L_3	P, S, R	L_4- 8275	1884
2			L_4	P, S, R	L_3- 8575	2024
3	L_1	L_3	L_2	P, S, R	L_4- 7900	2008
4			L_4	P, S, R	L_2- 8575	2146
5	L_1	L_4	L_2	P, S, R	L_3- 7900	2181
6			L_3	P, S, R	L_2- 8275	2179
7	L_3	L_1	L_2	P, S, R	L_4- 9660	1655
8			L_4	P, S, R	$L_2-10,335$	1781
9	L_3	L_2	L_1	X	X	X
10			L_4	P, S, R	$L_1-10,335$	1486 ◀—
11	L_3	L_4	L_1	X	X	X
12			L_2	P, S, R	L_1- 9660	1671

Calculation of investment-cost ratios from Table 8–24 reveals that only policies 1, 3, 7, and 10 warrant consideration as possible optimum solutions. It was determined that policy 10 is the optimum solution by rate of return analysis. The calculations for comparing policy 3 and policy 10 were performed in the following manner:

Let

$P =$ The additional investment required to implement policy 10 rather than policy 3

$R =$ The annual reduction in materials handling cost resulting from the implementation of policy 10 rather than policy 3

$n =$ The number of interest periods or useful life of materials handling equipment

$i =$ The interest rate at which the present worth of P and R is considered equal

$(USPW)_n{}^i =$ The uniform series present worth factor.

Then

$P = R(USPW)_n{}^i$

$P = R \dfrac{(1+i)^n - 1}{i(1+i)^{-n}}$

$P = 10{,}335 - 7900 = \$2435$

$R = 12(2008 - 1486) = \$6264$

$n = 6.$

In this case, i, the rate of return, was calculated to be approximately 266 percent, indicating that policy 10 is preferred to policy 3.

The optimal policy based on maximum rate of return was determined in the same manner as for minimum cost and is pointed out by arrow in Tables 8–22, 8–23, and 8–24. This policy is summarized in Table 8–25.

TABLE 8–25

Optimal Overall Policy Based on Maximum Rate of Return

Facility	Location Assigned	Flow Path	System Selected	Monthly Operating Cost	Capital Expenditure
A	L_3	$A{-}F_{III}$	T	$ 238	$ 1760
		$A{-}I$	P	150	5000
		$A{-}F_{II}$	P	114	0
C	L_2	$C{-}F_{II}$	P	128	0
		$C{-}F_{IV}$	R	315	2000
		$C{-}A$	R	160	0
B	L_4	$B{-}A$	P	228	0
		$B{-}F_I$	S	63	1575
		$B{-}F_{IV}$	R	90	0
Total				$1486	$10,335

In practice, the solutions obtained under the selected decision criteria should be compared to determine the preferred solution. The initial investment required to implement the optimal minimum cost policy exceeds the initial investment required for the optimal maximum rate of return policy by $6145. The annual materials handling cost under the minimum cost criterion is $2352 less than for the latter policy. This means that an annual rate of return of approximately 30 percent is obtained on the additional money required to implement the minimum cost policy. If this interest rate exceeds the minimum attractive rate of return required on invested capital, then the minimum cost criterion has provided the preferred solution.

REVIEW QUESTIONS

1. What criterion does Wimmert use in measuring arrangement effectiveness? What assumptions are inherent in application of Wimmert's method?
2. List the steps followed in applying Wimmert's method of arrangement.
3. How are the restrictions of Wimmert's method relaxed, for example, to adapt it to office layouts? What dangers are inherent in using factors of proximity desirability?
4. How does Armour and Buffa's algorithm improve on Wimmert's method? How do Armour and Buffa incorporate cost? Are there any dangers in handling cost in this manner? If so, what?
5. How does the situation under which level curves may be applied differ from the situation under which Wimmert's and Armour and Buffa's methods can be applied?
6. What restrictions are encountered in applying assignment model linear programming to plant arrangement?
7. How does LACH differ from the other methods of plant arrangement?
8. What may be the effect of treating the facility having the highest total volume as the first stage of the dynamic programming problem? Would you expect this to negate the effectiveness of the procedure under normal situations? Why or why not?

PROBLEMS

1. We have available a square area 200 feet on a side.
   a) If we want to assign 4 departments each 50 ft. x 50 ft. to the area by Wimmert's method, what are the optimum assignments if the load matrix is the same as the "L" matrix on page 99?
   b) Using the volume and sequence data of Figure 7–1 and given:
      (1) areas of *A*, *C*, *D*, and *E* are equal
      (2) areas of *B* and *F* are equal and each equal to the sum of the areas of *A*, *C*, *D* and *E*.
      (3) stores and stock areas are equal and one-half of *B*.
      What should be the arrangement using the extension of Wimmert's method?
   c) If aisles form the parameter of each department of areas given in (*b*) and handling costs are as given in the table on page 116, what is the best arrangement using LACH?

Chapter 9

PRODUCTION LINE
BALANCING
CONSIDERATIONS

WHEN A PROCESS is being designed for a single item or group of items (manufacturing or office) the problem reduces to one of balancing the work stations in the production line. This is similar to the problem of balancing an assembly line, only the operations may involve both fabricating and assembly rather than assembly alone. Most of the research related to systems of the line balancing type has been concerned with assembly line balancing. In the following discussion, however, it is assumed that the line being considered may be either production or assembly.

PRODUCT ARRANGEMENT LINE BALANCING

Before beginning our discussion of line balancing it is pointed out that some level of storage will normally be required between successive work stations. Even for assembly accomplished along a series of conveyor paced stations, buffer storage is often provided at, and between, work stations to allow for fluctuations in individual work station cycle times. Even though average time for all stations may be the same, operation time at each station is in fact a random variable. It is desired that each operation be assigned to a work station alone, or in combination with operations immediately preceding or succeeding to result in all work stations having equal average times to perform their work cycles. Assignment of work elements to a work station may then be varied as the required level of production on the line changes.

Balancing in the crudest manner can be accomplished by first establishing a fixed sequence of operation elements. The line is then balanced by combining successive elements toward the bound of work station cycle time which is established by dividing the total required production for the time period by the length of the time period.

TABLE 9–1

Fixed Operation Sequence Balances

Element (Operation) No.	Element Time in Minutes	100% Production 1000/8 hrs.	Task Time in Minutes	80% Production 800/8 hrs.	Task Time in Minutes	50% Production 500/8 hrs.	Task Time
1 .... 0.76		Operation 1 2 operators	0.38	Operation 1 2 operators	0.38	Operation 1 1 operator	0.76
2 .... 1.80		Operation 2 4 operators	0.45	Operation 2 3 operators	0.60	Operation 2 2 operators	0.90
3 .... 1.09		Operation 3 2 operators	0.36	Operation 3 2 operators	0.545	Operation 3 3 operators	1.00
4 .... 1.30		Operation 4 3 operators	0.473	Operation 4 3 operators	0.473	...	...
5 .... 0.12		...	...	...	...	...	...
6 .... 0.48		Operation 5 1 operator	0.48	Operation 5 1 operator	0.48	...	...
Total operators ..	13		...	11	...	6	...
Allowed cycle time (minutes) .		$\frac{480}{1000} = 0.48$		$\frac{480}{800} = 0.6$		$\frac{480}{500} = 0.96$	

This method of balancing is illustrated in Table 9–1. Note in this case there is $\frac{0.48 - 0.36}{36} = 33\frac{1}{3}$ percent variation in standard time for task assignments at 100 percent production levels. There is 31 percent variation at 50 percent production and the average labor cost per piece will be less at 50 percent production. Note also that operation 3 at 50 percent production has a standard time required of one minute while the allowed time is only 0.96 minute. Rather than assign another operator an attempt will be made to get increased production from the operators on this operation.

Note the above procedure assumes the fixed sequence of operations must be maintained. Fortunately, this usually is not necessary although a sequence of operations may be necessary for portions of the total assembly. However, some operations can be performed any time after some preceding operation and prior to some later operation. For example, the name plate on an electric motor can be attached any time after the case on which it is to be placed is completed and before the motor is enclosed in a further assembly or is packaged. Other operations may have conditions which make it uneconomical to vary the sequence. For example, if four bolts are located in a particular area of the assembly, it is possible to have each of four men drive one bolt. However, to do this each man must move his tool to the area and then return it to the between-operation position. One man, on the other hand, can drive all four bolts while working in the area, thereby saving the major portion of the tool-move time, making one man to four bolts more economical. To go one step further, it may be possible to drive the four bolts simultaneously with a special tool.

It may also be possible to perform a given operation at various work stations in the process, but there may be an optimum location which if deviated from will result in the cost of performing the operation increasing. This situation exists when two operations may be performed by the same operator, but in order to do so he must change positions. In this case, the added time required to change position must be included when the two operations are combined, and compared to the cost of performing the operations separately at two work stations. (Note as one alternative that the same operator might be used but parts would be permitted to accumulate before the operator changes position.)

Each of the assembly conditions discussed above are variations of precedence relationships. Operation *A* must precede operation *B*; operation *B* must precede operation *A*; or there may be no technological significance as to which precedes the other. If precedence relationship requirements are established, greater flexibility in combinations of operations for balancing result, thereby reducing variation between task times.

Precedence relationships may be presented graphically in the manner illustrated in Figure 9–1.

FIGURE 9–1

Operations Precedence Network (Graph)

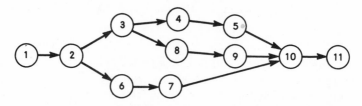

This signifies that operation 2 must follow operation 1. Operation 3 or 6 may follow operation 2. After operation 3 either operation 4 or 8 may be performed. Operation 7 must follow 6, 5 must follow 4, and 9 must follow 8. Furthermore, operations 5, 7, and 9 must all be completed prior to operation 10 which must precede 11. So long as these precedence conditions are maintained, any combination of task assignments may be made.

When a conveyorized line (*e.g.*, stations located on and paced by a conveyor) is used, all operations required before a station must be performed prior to arrival at that station. However, any operation which must succeed, or which is not directly related in precedence to the operation at the station, may be combined with the station so long as the combined task time does not exceed the cycle time necessary to satisfy required production levels.

Any operation can be combined with any other operation so long as all intermediate required operations between the two operations on any path of the precedence graph have been included in the task. Furthermore, any combination made must result in a task time equal to or less than the task time limit set by the cycle time necessary to meet production quantities.

In assembly line balancing, if assemblies are evenly spaced on the conveyor, the time in minutes per cycle is equal to the reciprocal of conveyor speed in fpm divided by assembly spacing in feet. The longest task time can be no greater than this cycle time which in turn can be no shorter than the longest operation time. Note that if task time = cycle time = longest operation time, the longest operation is a task by itself without further combining with other operations. If cycle time is shorter than the longest task time the station for which the longer task is required cannot maintain the cycle pace and must either allow a portion of the units to pass without the work being completed, or must require conveyor stoppage until the work is completed. If the work is passed, succeeding operations cannot be accomplished due to the improper condition of arriving parts and, if the conveyor is stopped, the average cycle time is extended until it equals the average time for the slowest task or operation. An analogous condition can be seen as existing for any production line.[1]

As a result of the above conditions cycle time is normally set equal to or slightly less than that which will meet production requirements and equal to or slightly in excess of the longest operation time. It is then desired to assign operations to tasks in such a manner as to minimize total operator idle time, in order to maximize labor utilization and minimize labor cost per unit. If we express operation times as a fractional part of cycle time and combine operations to reduce total line idle time to less than cycle time, our balance is optimal since no further reduction in labor for the line can be realized. It should be readily apparent that several combinations may satisfy these conditions. This means that an exclusive optimal assignment may not be necessary, rather a number of optimum balances exist. Note that if total idle time for all alternative assignments exceeds cycle

---

[1] It can be shown by queuing theory that if the task time is equal to the required cycle time the queue preceding that task will approach infinity over the long run due to the inability of the task station to recover the time lost due to random down times. In practice this is avoided.

time the optimum cannot be determined in this manner and other techniques must be used. Some of these techniques will be discussed following an example in which an optimum can be reached by having total idle time less than cycle time. This determination using the example of Table 9–2:

First:
      Assign operation times as fractions of cycle time. Cycle time $c = 1$:

TABLE 9–2

Operation No.	Oper. Time Cycle Time	Operation No.	Oper. Time Cycle Time
1	0.5	7	0.3
2	0.7	8	0.5
3	0.3	9	0.7
4	0.7	10	1.0
5	0.4	11	0.8
6	0.6		

Second:
      A special chart is constructed incorporating the various possible combinations of operations into tasks which satisfy both precedence and time restrictions. This chart for the example is given in Table 9–3 and is constructed in the following manner:

1. Three columnar headings are assigned. One for the number of the combination, one for the task time, and one for the idle time for the task combination. The first two are for reference purposes only and are not used in the analysis. Analysis utilizes idle time.

TABLE 9–3
Task Assignment Chart

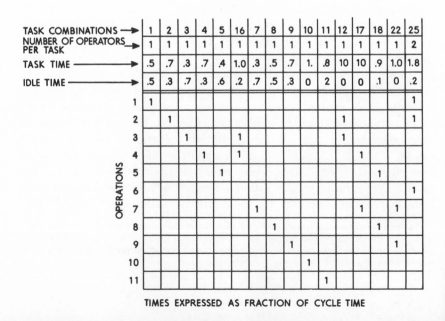

TASK COMBINATIONS →	1	2	3	4	5	16	7	8	9	10	11	12	17	18	22	25
NUMBER OF OPERATORS PER TASK →	1	1	1	1	1	1	1	1	1	1	1	1	1	1	1	2
TASK TIME →	.5	.7	.3	.7	.4	1.0	.3	.5	.7	1.	.8	10	10	.9	1.0	1.8
IDLE TIME →	.5	.3	.7	.3	.6	.2	.7	.5	.3	0	2	0	0	.1	0	.2
OPERATIONS 1	1															1
2		1											1			1
3			1		1							1				
4				1	1							1				
5						1							1			
6																1
7							1						1	1		
8								1					1			
9									1					1		
10										1						
11											1					

TIMES EXPRESSED AS FRACTION OF CYCLE TIME

2. List operations along the left side top to bottom.
3. Each operation can be assigned as a separate task, therefore, use these for the first alternatives 1 through 11, indicating operations assigned to a particular combination by entering a 1 in the corresponding row and column intersection.
4. Continue establishing combinations by assigning operation times to combinations in such a manner that neither precedence or time restrictions are voided. To accomplish this combine operations in which total time $\le$ cycle time, then check combinations against the precedence chart to determine allowability under precedence restrictions. Continue until all apparent combinations are incorporated.

Third:

Develop a tentative solution matrix similar to Table 9–4 in the following manner:
1. Select the combination with the lowest idle time. In case of a tie, make an arbitrary selection from among those with lowest idle time.
2. Record the column data of this combination in the tentative solution matrix.
3. Select another combination with lowest idle time which does not include the row or operations previously recorded in the tentative solution matrix and record this combination data in the tentative solution matrix. Continue until all operations appear in the solution matrix.

TABLE 9–4
Tentative Solution Matrix I

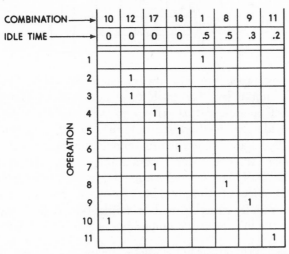

COMBINATION →	10	12	17	18	1	8	9	11
IDLE TIME →	0	0	0	0	.5	.5	.3	.2
1					1			
2		1						
3		1						
4			1					
5				1				
6				1				
7			1					
8						1		
9							1	
10	1							
11								1

(OPERATION)

Fourth:

Determine whether the tentative solution is optimal by comparing the sum of idle times to line cycle time. If Σ idle time $\ge c$ a better solution may be possible. If Σ idle time $< c$, the solution is optimal and the solution acceptable. For this trial example, the sum of idle time $= 0.5 + 0.5 + 0.3 + 0.2 = 1.5 > 1$ and a better solution may be possible.

The steps are repeated to arrive at another possible solution represented by Table 9–5. The sum of idle time for this trial is $0.2 + 0.5 < 1$ and therefore the solution is optimal. Note, however, in order to accomplish this, combination 25 includes two stations on the line. This can be accomplished by switching of alternate assemblies to each task station. The task assignments on the precedence graph will appear as indicated in Figure 9–2. The underlined numbers indicate the sequence on the line of tasks to maintain precedence relationships.

TABLE 9–5

Tentative Solution Matrix II

COMBINATION ⟶	16	10	11	25	18	22
IDLE TIME ⟶	0	0	.2	.2	.1	0
1				1		
2				1		
3	1					
4	1					
5					1	
6			1			
7						1
8					1	
9						1
10		1				
11			1			

(OPERATION — vertical axis label, rows 1–11)

The preceding procedure will always guarantee an optimal balance when total idle time is less than cycle time. However, for systems with a large number of operations this criteria may not be realizable and the procedure provides no method for determining an optimum balance. Salveson[2] and Bowman[3] use linear programming models to determine the optimum balance. Integer linear programming assures a task being assigned to one and only one station. Although model optimality is assured, the size of the problem (both in number of variables and number of equations) increases rapidly with the number of operations under consideration. For this reason the linear programming approach is of more interest from

[2] M. E. Salveson, "The Assembly Line Balancing Problem" *Journal of Industrial Engineering*, Vol. 6, No. 3 (May–June, 1955), pp. 18–25.

[3] E. H. Bowman, "Assembly Line Balancing by Linear Programming," *Operations Research*, Vol. 8, No. 3 (May–June, 1960), pp. 385–89.

FIGURE 9–2

Task Assignments on Conveyor-Paced Assembly Line

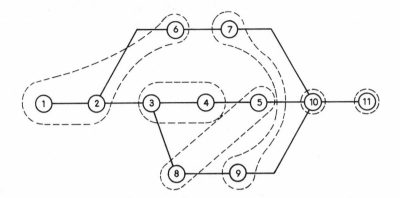

the academic standpoint rather than the practicability of the procedure for use. For those interested in pursuing the linear programming approach, Salveson's and Bowman's writing as well as White's[4] improvements on Bowman's model are recommended. For our discussion we will look at three procedural approaches which provide solutions which under certain conditions will provide optimum balance but which do not necessarily guarantee optimum. However, procedurally each is somewhat easier to follow for manual calculations and the last two are adaptable to computer solution with less capacity restriction than that of the linear programming approach.

The first method is that of Jackson[5] which provides the minimum number of stations for a given cycle time by looking successively at all feasible combinations of operations to successive work stations until a balance has been obtained. This method is satisfactory for hand calculation of balance for a few operations. As the number of operations increases, the difficulty of the procedure increases due to the likelihood of failing to observe all combinations. Use of Jackson's method for computer solution, however, is difficult due to the necessity for eliminating duplicate combinations and checking for dominance as the procedure continues. The model is optimized by the procedure.

Jackson's basic idea is relatively simple. First, determine all feasible first work stations by determining the operation combinations which satisfy precedence constraints without exceeding the selected cycle time. Second, for each of the feasible first stations, determine the allowable second stations which satisfy the precedence and cycle time constraints. This is

[4] W. W. White, "Comments on a Paper by Bowman," *Operations Research*, Vol. 9, No. 2 (March–April, 1961), pp. 274–76.

[5] J. R. Jackson, "A Computing Procedure for a Line Balancing Problem," *Management Science*, Vol. 2, No. 3 (April, 1956), pp. 261–271.

continued until all operations have been assigned in a single sequence. The number of work stations required for the earliest inclusion of all operations is the minimum number of work stations required to balance the line. The number of combinations of operations which it is necessary to construct are reduced by following rules of dominance and equivalency indicated below. As an example of Jackson's method we will balance our earlier operations given in Table 9–2 and show it as Figure 9–3.

FIGURE 9–3

Stations

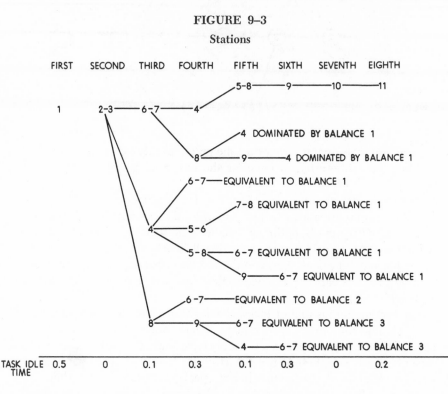

NOTE: Small numbers below station columns are operation idle times as fractions of cycle time.

Note that the balance using Jackson's method in the example results in eight stations and eight operators which is one more operator than by the previous balance method. This is due primarily to the lack of the ability to determine possible combinations of operations to establish two identical parallel task stations as was done previously.

The next line balancing technique we want to look at is the ranked positional weight technique as proposed by Helgeson and Birnie.[6] The positional weight of an operation is its required time plus the time required

[6] W. P. Helgeson, and D. P. Birnie, "Assembly Line Balancing Using the Ranked Positional Weight Technique," *Journal of Industrial Engineering*, Vol. 12, No. 6 (November–December, 1961), pp. 394–98.

to complete all operations which must succeed it. In order to apply the technique the following steps are followed:

1. Determine the positional weight for all operations.
2. Record the operation(s) which immediately precedes each operation.
3. Rank the operations based upon the weight in step 1 with highest weight ranked first.
4. Proceed to assign operations to tasks, assigning the highest weight and rank first.
5. If at any task station additional time remains after assignment of an operation assign the next succeeding ranked operation to the task so long as the operation does not violate precedence relationships or does not exceed the remaining available time at the task station.

We now apply the above steps to the data of Table 9–2 as used previously. Weighting is given in Table 9–6.

TABLE 9–6
Positional Weights of Operations for Balance

Operation	1	2	3	4	5	6	7	8	9	10	11
Positional weight	6.5	6.0	4.4	2.9	2.2	2.7	2.1	3.0	2.5	1.8	0.8
Immediate preceders		1	2	3	4	2	6	3	8	7,5,9	10

NOTE: The ratio $\dfrac{\text{Operational time}}{\text{Cycle time}}$ is again used. Times in the table could be standard or average and the cycle time selected would then be the limit for combining rather than 1.

The positional weight ranks of the operations are: 1 (6.5); 2 (6.0); 3 (4.4); 8 (3.0); 4 (2.9); 6 (2.7); 9 (2.5); 5 (2.2); 7 (2.1); 10 (1.8); and 11 (0.87). The number in parenthesis is the positional weight for the operation. The resulting balance becomes:

Task number	1	2	3	4	5	6	7	8
Operation	1	2,3	4	5,6	7,8	9	10	11
Task idle time as fraction of cycle time	0.5	0	0.3	0	0.2	0.3	0	0.2

Note that the number of tasks is the same as that obtained using Jackson's combinatorial approach but the operations are combined differently for individual tasks. Although either procedure may have the larger idle time it happens in this example that the ranked positional weight technique has 0.2 cycle time greater total idle time. The important thing to observe, however, is that in both cases the total idle time exceeds the cycle time. This indicates the possibility of an improved balance which by our initial precedence based balance we know exists. However, note further that only one station in excess of optimum exists indicating that the heuristic techniques approach optimum. Since for a larger problem it would be extremely difficult, if not impossible, to combine in such a manner that the sum of idle time will be less than cycle time the heuristic technique's ability to approach optimum becomes very important. By the heuristic approaches we will improve the likelihood of obtaining or approaching the optimum. Traditional balancing methods or chance balance methods do not provide this assurance of good balance.

The last method of balancing we are going to look at is that of Moodie and Young.[7] Moodie and Young introduce a two-phase balancing procedure for constant operation times and also provide a means for balancing when variation in operation times are considered. For variable operations the assumption of statistically independent normally distributed times for operations is made. The assumption of independence and normalcy is justified by empirical data collected by Moodie and Young and also the results of earlier investigations by others considering operator time distributions. Since the two-phase balancing procedure will usually provide an optimum balance the procedure permits inclusion of variable time data, and is readily adaptable to computer solution. The procedure of Moodie and Young is presented in somewhat greater detail than the above heuristic procedures.

Before beginning the discussion we redefine the operation times to minutes and the data of Table 9–2 now appears as

Operation No.	Time in Minutes	Operation No.	Time in Minutes
1	0.5	7	0.3
2	0.7	8	0.5
3	0.3	9	0.7
4	0.7	10	1.0
5	0.4	11	0.8
6	0.6		

and the precedence relationships remain the same. Phase I of the method consists of assigning operations to consecutive tasks, from task 1 to the final task by the "largest candidate rule." The largest candidate being the next available operation with maximum operation time. Note that the candidate must continue to satisfy all precedence restrictions. Moodie and Young have developed predecessor (P) and follower (F) matrices to facilitate candidate assignment. The P matrix rows contain the operation numbers of immediately preceding operations and the F matrix rows the operation numbers of the immediately following operations. Using our example the P and F matrices are shown in Table 9–7.

---

[7] C. L. Moodie, and H. H. Young, "A Heuristic Method of Assembly Line Balancing for Assumptions of Constant or Variable Work Element Times," *Journal of Industrial Engineering*, Vol. 16, No. 1 (January–February, 1965), pp. 23–29.

Assignment of operations to tasks is made in the following manner (it is important to note that the logic involved in operation assignment by the matrices is directly adaptable to computer logic):

TABLE 9-7
P and F Matrices for Example Problem

For Operation Number	Immediately Preceding Operations			For Operation Number	Immediately Following Operations	
1	0	0	0	1	2	0
2	1	0	0	2	3	6
3	2	0	0	3	4	8
4	3	0	0	4	5	0
5	4	0	0	5	10	0
6	2	0	0	6	7	0
7	6	0	0	7	10	0
8	3	0	0	8	9	0
9	8	0	0	9	10	0
10	5	7	9	10	11	0
11	10	0	0	11	0	0
	P matrix				*F matrix*	

a) Note the rows in P which contain all zeros.

b) Assign the largest of the operations found in (a) if a selection is required.

c) Denote the operation number in the rows of F denoted by the operation assigned in (a) and (b).

d) Go to the rows of P identified as the operation numbers denoted in the F matrix in (c)—replace the operation number of the operation assigned in (a) and (b) by zero.

e) Continue until all operations are assigned to tasks.

Applying the above steps results in:

Task number	1	2	3	4	5	6	7	8
Operations assigned	1	2,3	4	6,5	8,7	9	10	11
Task time	0.5	1	0.7	1	0.8	0.7	1	0.8
Cycle time	1	1	1	1	1	1	1	1
Idle time	0.5	0	0.3	0	0.2	0.3	0	0.2

Sum of task idle times = 1.5 > cycle time = 1.

Another characteristic of the Moodie and Young method can be pointed out. Note that the sum of the task idle times exceeds the cycle times, which is taken as the longest task time or one minute. This indicates that an optimum or more nearly optimum solution may be possible. Incrementing the cycle time will aid in reaching the optimum balance. In our example if we raise the cycle time to 1.1 minutes and repeat the balance we obtain:

Task number	1	2	3	4	5	6	7
Operation assigned	1	2,3	4,5	6,8	9,7	10	11
Task time	0.5	1	1.1	1.1	1	1	0.8
Cycle time	1.1	1.1	1.1	1.1	1.1	1.1	1.1
Idle time	0.6	0.1	0	0	0.1	0.1	0.3

Sum of task idle times = 1.2 > cycle time = 1.1.

If the procedure of increasing the cycle time by one increment is continued until cycle time = 1.5, we obtain a balance:

Task number	1	2	3	4	5
Operation assigned	1,2,3	6,7,8	4,9	5,10	11
Task time	1.5	1.4	1.4	1.4	0.8
Cycle time	1.5	1.5	1.5	1.5	1.5
Idle time	0	0.1	0.1	0.1	0.7

Sum of task idle time = 1 < cycle time 1.5.

By the earlier argument when the sum of idle time is less than the cycle time the balance is optimum for the selected cycle time. Note, however, that although we earlier found the optimum when the cycle time was one minute to be seven stations, if we increase the cycle time to 1.5 we have a direct procedure to reduce the stations to five. The labor cost per unit at a cycle time of 1.5 minutes is greater than at a cycle time of one for seven stations, since $(1.5 \times 5) > (1 \times 7)$ but there was no way to assure us getting to the seven stations by a direct route. The unit labor cost increase at a cycle time of 1.5 minutes is only $\dfrac{7.5 - 7.0}{7} = \dfrac{1}{14}$, which is closer than we have been able to get by the other methods. This indicates the rule of increasing cycle time by an increment until the balance is optimum for the cycle time being considered will result in optimum or close optimum being possible for any assembly line.

Although it does not result in any improvement in our example problem, Moodie and Young suggest a second phase in the balance which may secure an optimum balance at a cycle time less than that obtained by phase 1. This is accomplished by systematically searching for possible trades of operations between tasks which will tend to equalize task idle times. The phase 2 procedure is as follows:

a) Determine GOAL where,
$$\text{GOAL} = \frac{\text{Maximum Task Time} - \text{Minimum Task Time}}{2}$$

b) Trade single operations of the maximum task which are less than 2 × GOAL for operations in the minimum task which will not violate precedence restrictions and result in a gain to the minimum task of less than 2 × GOAL.

c) If necessary to continue trades attempt to make a trade of operations between the minimum task and second maximum task, third maximum, and so forth, until the minimum task has been compared with all others. Repeat with the second minimum until all combinations are checked.

Flow charts for computation of phase 1 and phase 2 as designed by Moodie and Young are reproduced in Figure 9–4.

Balance when Operation Times Are Not Considered Constant

Moodie and Young present a method for preparing line balances under

FIGURE 9–4a
Flow Chart—Phase 1 of Heuristic Method

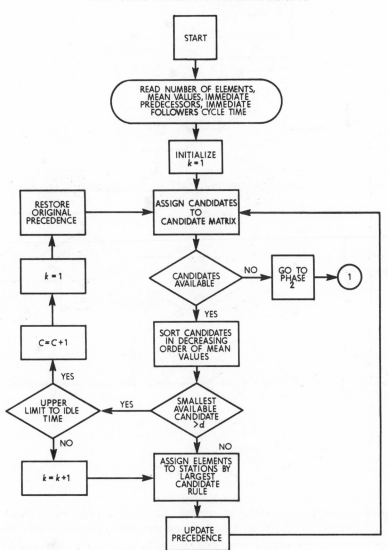

FIGURE 9–4b

Flow Chart—Phase 2 of Heuristic Method

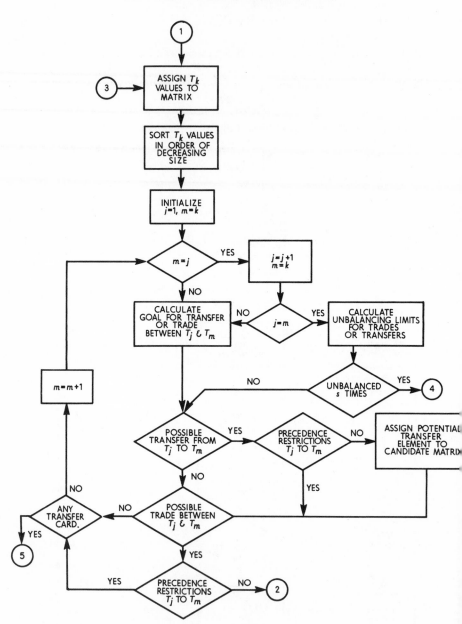

probabilistic criteria. In order to accomplish this it is assumed individual operation times are distributed as independent normal random variables. The assumption permits additivity of operation variances to arrive at task

FIGURE 9–4b, *Continued*

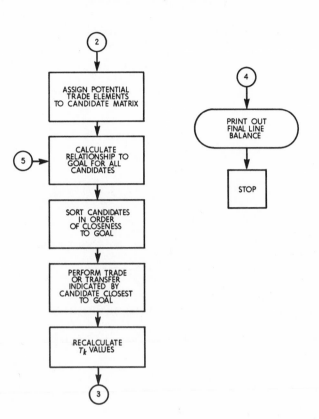

variances. Also, the distribution of the sum of individual normal random variables follows a normal distribution. This permits one-tailed tests of hypothesis relating to the probability of completing a task in a given time using tables of the area under the standardized normal distribution. For example, letting T_k represent task time providing desired confidence of completion, and C, cycle time, $T_k = \sum_{i\epsilon k} E(O_i) + \Theta \sqrt{\sum_{i\epsilon k} \mathrm{Var}(O_i)}$ where O_i is the time for operation $i\epsilon k$ and Θ is the number of standard deviations above the expected value of the task time necessary to provide the one-tailed confidence. This is represented in Figure 9–5. The result of considering variability from independent normal operation times is that the optimizing objective of phase 1 and phase 2 becomes:

$$\mathrm{Min} \sum_{k=1}^{K} \left[C - \left(\sum_{i\epsilon k} E(O_i) + \Theta \sqrt{\sum_{i\epsilon k} \mathrm{Var}(O_i)} \right) \right]$$

where k is the number of tasks on the line. The procedure is identical but with the substitution of the variable data criteria for the constant value criteria which can be written, $\text{Min} \sum\limits_{k=1}^{K} \left(C - \sum\limits_{i \in k} E(O_i) \right)$.

FIGURE 9–5

Relationships between $E(T_{\text{Task}})$, T_k, and Cycle Time under Variability

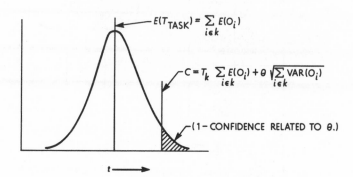

LINE BALANCING APPLIED TO PRODUCTION LINES

Two principal problems exist in applying line balancing to production lines:

1. Element combinations may be defined by machine factors rather than operator factors.
2. A continuous conveyor does not pace the line.

If 1 occurs the machine defined operation may be treated as an element in the precedence chart. If 2 occurs line balancing techniques may be used to gain added insight into balance but will not be directly applicable. Further, unless conveyor paced, batching of one type or another occurs. For example, if trucks are used to move goods between operations movement occurs for a unit load and not individual pieces. Therefore, a buffer of unit loads will occur between stations. Unless a new unit load is provided before work on the preceding load is complete delay occurs. If gravity conveyors are used, they transfer material automatically but do not pace the line since fixed distance is not maintained between units. Therefore, it is usually necessary that buffers exist prior to each station on the line to minimize delays. The objective in these cases tends to minimization of cost of buffer stock.

For automated production lines, defined usually as highly mechanized lines, conveyors and automatic transfer devices are used between operations. It is desirable in this case to have all operations as nearly equal in length as possible. Line balancing can be used to achieve this. However, the travel time from the "discharge" point of one operation to the "pickup" point of the next operation is waste time and must be added to the operation or cycle time (both are in effect equal on an automated line) unless a buffer of at least one unit is maintained between stations. The buffer of one permits movement from the discharge point to the pickup point to occur during the operation on the preceding item. If time between discharge and pickup exceeds the cycle time two or more units must be in buffer.

Note that the above discussion relating to automated production is also applicable to assembly line balancing if a conveyor length interval occurs between work stations. If a buffer is not provided in these cases the travel time must be added to the operation succeeding or preceding travel.

In order to consider the effects which may result from queuing effects (buffer) between stations after balancing production lines (nonautomated) it is desirable to derive queuing models or use Monte Carlo simulation procedures to evaluate the balance effectiveness. Rebalance with proper allowance to reduce adverse queuing characteristics at critical stations may then be necessary.

REVIEW QUESTIONS

1. Why is some storage required between successive stations on an assembly or production line?
2. What is the principal objection to balancing by the crude traditional method illustrated in Table 9–1? When would this method be applicable?
3. What is the only true criterion for measuring optimality of a line balance? Why may there be a number of balances, each of which is optimal?
4. What is the significance of cycle time in line balance? Define cycle time.
5. Why is direct application of line balancing techniques limited to conveyor paced lines?
6. Explain Jackson's technique of line balancing. When and why might you use it?
7. Explain the positional weight as used in Helgeson and Birnie and its use in line balancing.
8. How does Moodie and Young's line balancing technique using fixed operation times differ from the other techniques? Is this as important as their ability to consider probabilistic criteria? Why or why not?
9. How does the production line balancing problem differ from the assembly line balancing problem?

PROBLEMS

1. Given the following precedence network and operation times for an assembly line design, balance the line by:

a) Jackson's combinatorial method,
b) Positional weight,
c) Moodie and Young's method
for 100 units per hour output of the line.

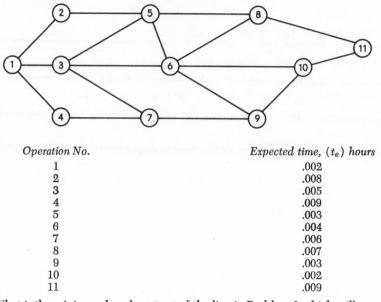

Operation No.	Expected time, (t_e) hours
1	.002
2	.008
3	.005
4	.009
5	.003
6	.004
7	.006
8	.007
9	.003
10	.002
11	.009

2. What is the minimum hourly output of the line in Problem 1 which will permit a guarantee of optimum balance?

PART III

Plant and Equipment Maintenance

Chapter 10

THE NATURE OF THE

MAINTENANCE PROBLEM

ALL PHYSICAL FACILITIES on plant property are susceptible to failure (breakdown) or deterioration due to natural causes of age or the effects of use. Causes of deterioration or failure may be internal to the equipment or due to external factors. Failure results in expense to replace or repair the facility itself as well as possible losses in production or services if output is critical or maintenance excessive. Costs may also be due to resulting idleness of allied equipment and/or personnel. Steps may be taken to maintain a level of maintenance of the facilities which will reduce the likelihood of failure to a minimum. (Note that no degree of maintenance will prevent failure; for example, start-up or infant failure may be reduced by zero-defect programs but cannot be totally eliminated.) However, maintenance to prevent failure—usually designated as preventive maintenance —involves significant expense itself. If the only objective is to prevent failure, excessive moneys may be spent to conduct the preventive maintenance program and the cost of prevention will exceed the cost of failure. However, as with most, if not all, cost-oriented plant activities there exists a break-even point on the failure-maintenance cost curve which establishes the optimum balance between the level of preventive maintenance provided and the effect of failure. Before looking at some methods which can assist in determining this break-even point we briefly review the nature of the maintenance problem and some factors and characteristics which must be considered in analyzing the problem and designing the desirable program.

Maintenance Efficiency

Maintenance efficiency without further definition of the criteria for measuring efficiency is meaningless. From the standpoint of operations, maintenance is efficient if it prevents breakdown, or if breakdown occurs it returns the equipment which failed to service in the minimum time. From the labor control standpoint, maintenance is efficient if all maintenance personnel are working at the standard level of effort at all times without exceeding reasonable idle time necessary to overcome fatigue and satisfy personal demands. From the cost control standpoint, the efficiency of maintenance may be measured by the maintenance department's ability to remain within its established materials and labor budget. The safety director considers maintenance efficient when there are no accidents which can be assigned to machine or equipment causes. Each of these criteria are real and each is reasonable—with reservations. The reservation is that none of the criteria can properly be considered independent of the others. Therefore, under each of the criteria a significant level of inefficiency will exist to permit maximization of the joint efficiency. As a result of traditional measurement being by independent factors, maintenance is often considered inherently inefficient. To be realistic, however, we must define what is meant by inherent inefficiency. In simplest terms it merely means that none of the traditional criteria or measures of efficiency can be used independently because by their individual natures they are in conflict with one another. For example, to satisfy production's criteria of preventing breakdown or in case of breakdown returning equipment to service as rapidly as possible creates inefficiency by the other criteria. Staffing of maintenance personnel must be high to provide rapid service at time of breakdown. Since breakdown occurs randomly, maintenance would need to be staffed for maximum demand, automatically creating excessive labor idleness during lower than maximum demand periods, and thereby significantly lowering labor control's measure of efficiency. At the same time in order to get a piece of equipment which has failed back into service as rapidly as possible, temporary measures may be taken for the equipment to perform satisfactorily until the next period the equipment is scheduled to be idle at which time permanent repair can be made. Frequently temporary repair increases the safety hazard, thereby reducing the safety criteria of the safety director. At the same time excessive staffing, remaintenance for permanence following temporary maintenance repair, and the necessity for carrying high inventories of replacement parts to assure rapid repair will increase the costs, thereby reducing efficiency from the standpoint of cost control. Similar analogous effects can be thought of for the remaining criteria if any of the other single criteria were to be maximized. Until rather recently decisions as to the trade off between efficiencies was often rather arbitrary dependent upon the background of those in management responsible for decision and at best only qualitative balance techniques were used. With a systems approach using total cost as the criteria it is possible today for management to balance traditional criteria. There will continue to exist a conflict between those responsible for the traditional independent measurements, each likely to exert pressures on management to give more consideration to their criteria at the sacrifice of all others. Only continuous evaluation and review using accurate data will permit management to properly balance the inherent inefficiencies.

Some Types of Decision Required Relative to Maintenance

The major types of decisions relative to maintenance (see Figure 10–1) may be classified as:

1. Preventive versus failure maintenance.
2. Internal or external service personnel.
3. Repair versus replace.
4. Contract versus single incident negotiation for external services.
5. Replacement parts inventory.
6. Maintenance job assignment control.

Although this list is nowhere near complete, it does represent six of the critical areas of any maintenance program. Each will be discussed briefly. Certain techniques, which are adaptable for decision making, will be considered more fully in the next chapter.

FIGURE 10–1

Maintenance Decision Network

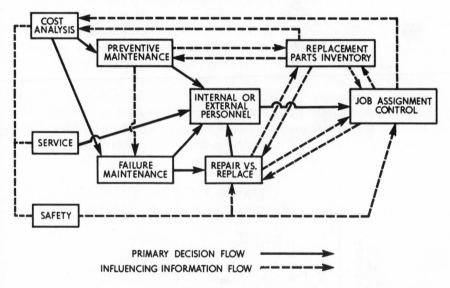

PRIMARY DECISION FLOW ⟶

INFLUENCING INFORMATION FLOW ⤍⤍⤍⤍➤

1. *Preventive versus Failure Maintenance.* It might be said that "natural" maintenance is maintenance to repair something which has failed. Few industries could afford natural maintenance today. Failure is expensive both in direct and indirect costs. Seldom does one component of a facility fail without causing the immediate failure of a related component or else an adverse effect on the related component which may reduce the related component's "time to failure." Although this effect may be difficult or impossible to measure, it exists. The effect of this related failure is often disregarded in failure analysis mathematics by the assumption of independent failure of components and results in an error between theoretical system failure rate and the actual failure rate determined from system historical or sample data.

In addition to the adverse effect on other components of the system, failure often results in damage to material in process at the time of failure and depending upon the nature of failure may create a hazard to personnel. Furthermore, production schedules are disrupted reducing the effectiveness of other facilities and associated personnel, thereby increasing cost of operation. In addition, component(s) replacement or major repair is probably mandatory after failure and unless the replacement part is on hand immediately, the period for which the facility is "down" is lengthened, which increases the magnitude of adverse cost effects throughout associated facilities.

To overcome or reduce these adverse effects and associated increased costs management provides for preventive maintenance. Preventive maintenance is any maintenance performed to reduce the likelihood of failure. In its simplest form preventive maintenance may be nothing more than daily oiling or greasing of bearings to prevent their burnout and the associated damage to the facility. At the other extreme, preventive maintenance may be periodic removal of the facility from service in order to perform a complete rebuild of the facility. Between the two extremes may be a number of inspection, evaluation, and action procedures to reduce failure likelihood between major rebuilds and to increase the time between successive rebuilds. In attempting to reduce failure, the extent of these preventive maintenance operations can become so great that their cost exceeds that of failure. It is management's objective to determine where the break-even between failure costs and preventive maintenance costs occur.

The break-even cost relationship is illustrated in Figure 10–2.

FIGURE 10–2

Preventive Maintenance Cost per Unit Produced or Unit Time Period

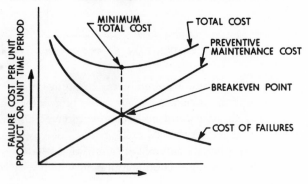

Note that although preventive maintenance may be added or deleted resulting in an approximately linear maintenance cost curve, the rate of reduction in failure costs as preventive maintenance costs increase drops rapidly and is asymtotic. The objective is to find the level of preventive maintenance, P^*, which results in a cost of preventive maintenance $P_c^* = F_c^*$, the cost of failure at P^*.

Now, the cost of failure $F_c = P(F) \cdot (C_F)$, the probability of failure times the cost of a failure if a failure occurs. But, both $P(F)$ and C_F are dependent upon the level of preventive maintenance, P_{ML}, practiced, so that $F_C = \{P(F)(C_F)\} \mid P_{ML}$. If we convert this to a series of regression equations then:

$$P(F) = aP_{ML}$$
$$C_F = bP_{ML}$$

and

$$F_C = aP_{ML} \cdot bP_{ML} = abP^2_{ML}$$

The optimizing equation exists when P^*_{ML} is the P_{ML} which minimizes abP^2_{ML} where P^*_{ML} represents the optimum level of preventive maintenance to be performed and a and b are regression coefficients, not necessarily constants. The problem of measuring P_{ML} remains, but if it is established, for example, in man-hours of preventive maintenance assigned per unit time period, an approximation of the optimum level is feasible.

2. Use of Internal or External Service Personnel. The decision as to whether to provide the necessary maintenance personnel or facilities within the firm's organization or to utilize services external to the organization is primarily an economic decision. The problem arises in evaluating the economics of alternatives. For example, neither policy is likely to be best for all plant maintenance functions. However, one of the major costs of the firm doing the maintenance itself is the cost of labor. The cost of labor per hour of use will vary as the labor utilization varies. But difficulty may be experienced in incorporating this resulting cost variation in decision models. If individuals or crews are to be assigned to a specific set of maintenance operations, Monte Carlo or other simulation techniques may be used to either establish the economic crew size for fixed activities or the economic groups of maintenance operations for a fixed crew size by incrementing the variable until the minimum point on the total cost curve has been established. It remains, however, to compare the cost of this optimum to the cost of producing the same service externally. If considering staffing as the variable, the cost of external service may be considered as the cost of no staff on a permanent basis.

The costs associated with maintenance staffing when being compared to external services include:

1. Direct cost of full-time maintenance labor.
2. Indirect costs of full-time labor.
3. Cost of maintaining repair parts inventory in excess to that required if external services are used.

4. The value of reduced downtime for repair. In most cases use of in-plant service personnel will reduce time between breakdown and start of repair. However, this is not necessarily true since in-plant staffing may be less adequate to provide service on demand than the staff of the service organization. Monte Carlo, or other simulation is again appliable to determined frequency and length of delay.

5. Obsolescence costs. With certain equipment (particularly data processing equipment) rental and service are often combined in a single contract. If the equipment is purchased not only must the normal costs of owning and maintaining the equipment be compared to the rental and service cost, but consideration must be given to the probability of improved equipment becoming available which should be secured (but if secured would result in a significant loss on the present equipment). One method of allowing for this is to estimate the probable loss if present equipment is obsoleted and multiply this by the estimated probability of obsolescence in any year as the estimate of that year's cost of ownership due to the risk of obsolescence.

3. Repair versus Replace.   Again we are faced with a problem which is basically a question of economics. Replacement decision rules have been considered in this series in the book *The Capacity Decision System.* Here we will only review briefly relative to repair or replace. In review, certain basic principles of evaluation and decision under the replacement problem are:

a) Costs of prior investment for equipment, maintenance, or operation are sunk costs and do not influence present decision.

b) When comparing alternatives each alternative must be capable of satisfying process requirements for which it is being considered. If demands increase over the projected life of one alternative to a point that the alternative cannot satisfy demand the decision must be based upon replacement or supplementation to meet the excess demand at the time it occurs.

c) First cost or initial cost of equipment is installed cost ready to operate.

d) First cost of existing equipment is fair market value less removal cost plus any cost necessary to repair or convert to satisfy process demands.

e) Decision is based upon average annual cost which is the sum of investment costs (depreciation and return on investment), operating costs (labor and maintenance), and associated overhead (including taxes and insurance).

f) Value of production lost during change over (if not directly recoverable) is part of the first cost of the equipment causing the loss.

Now note that if the question of repair or replace arises, three alternatives are present, (*a*) keep present equipment in present condition, (*b*) repair present equipment, and (*c*) replace present equipment. Note further that (*b*) and (*c*) are, in fact, alternatives of replacement and the economics of each alternative can be determined following the rules above. Therefore, the problem of repair is, in fact, another replacement alternative and should be treated in the same manner as any other alternatives considered, using care to establish first cost and the useful life after repair.

4. Contract versus Single Incident Negotiation for External Services. Again, the basic problem is a problem of economics, similar in many respects to that of "internal or external service." Three primary cost influences arise: (*a*) total maintenance incidents over the decision time period, (*b*) the cost per maintenance incident, and (*c*) service effectiveness. The total maintenance incidents must be considered since it is likely that under a service contract provision may be made for certain preventive maintenance which will not be considered for individual incident contracts. Service effectiveness is primarily concerned with the value of delay of repair due to negotiation and scheduling single incident maintenance. Decision is based upon cost comparison where the costs of the two alternatives are:

1. Cost of contract maintenance = Cost of additional preventive maintenance + period cost of contract + (probability of breakdown during period) (value of lost time if breakdown occurs).
2. Cost of single incident contract = Cost of preventive maintenance + (probability of breakdown) (contract price for repair + value of lost time if breakdown occurs).

Note that both probability of breakdown and probable loss time in case of breakdown will be different under each policy and must be established independently for each alternative before comparison of policy costs.

5. Replacement Parts Inventory. Replacement parts inventories have the same costs associated with them as raw stores or finished parts inventory, *e.g.*, parts costs, space costs, ordering costs, and carrying costs. In addition, there is the cost of failure to have a part on hand when needed. This last may be sizable at the time of individual occurrence since the cost of failure to have the part may be the summation of all the costs associated with lost production. Various economic order quantity formulas have been presented in other booklets of the series and will not be repeated here in total; rather we will look at the model incorporating those considerations important to the spare parts problem.

The conditions which we will consider as representative of the spare parts problem are:

a) An outage (shortage) of the part may occur.
b) Discrete requirements must be satisfied.
c) Demand is discontinuous.
d) Demand is variable.
e) Reorder time is fixed and known.

Symbols of factors affecting total cost are:

d = Demand during time interval
Q = Order quantity
S = Inventory level at beginning of period
$P(d)$ = Probability of demand d during time interval

$C_1 =$ Holding cost per unit during time interval; a sum of all costs associated with carrying an inventory

$C_2 =$ Cost of a shortage.

The expected cost (EC) associated with any value of inventory level, S, is then:

$$(EC)_S = C_1 \sum_{d=0}^{S} P(d)(S-d) + C_2 \sum_{d=S+1}^{\infty} P(d)(d-S).$$

It can be shown that the optimum (minimum) expected cost occurs when S satisfies the following inequality:

$$P(d \le S_o - 1) < \frac{C_2}{C_1 + C_2} < P(d \le S_o)$$

where S_o represents the optimum stock level to be maintained. The problem remains to determine $P(d)$, C_1, and C_2 for the item being investigated. Manual determination of these values for an inventory of any size becomes prohibitive. Historical data in a computerized total data system can provide estimates of $P(d)$. Estimates of C_1 and C_2 must be determined from standard costs or cost records.

Note that if there exists an S_o such that:

$$P(d \le S_o) = \frac{C_2}{C_1 + C_2} \text{ or } P(d \le S_o - 1) = \frac{C_2}{C_1 + C_2}$$

there will be two optimums S_o and $(S_o + 1)$ or S_o and $(S_o - 1)$ respectively. Also C_2 in most instances will be a variable rather than a fixed cost. The expected value of C_2, $E(C_2)$ may be substituted for C_2 in the previous relationship for an estimate of optimum. If for a particular critical part the cost of a single failure due to an extensive delay is to be limited to some maximum C_2 under the recognition of variability of C_2, Monte Carlo simulation can be used to estimate the value of S for a desired confidence level of not exceeding the desired delay limit and the associated costs can be determined from the same Monte Carlo design. If the costs associated with maximum delay protection significantly differ from the general optimum given further analysis may be called for.

6. *Maintenance Job Assignment Control.* Before discussing maintenance job assignment control let's look first at cost objectives. The objective *is not* to minimize direct cost of maintenance; rather the objective *is* to minimize the total cost of maintenance and downtime. Downtime cost in this case includes any costs associated with, or resulting from, equipment being unable to perform at maximum effectiveness due to equipment condition. Income offsetting this cost is the value added to product when equipment is operating. If we are to minimize the real cost, it will usually be necessary to sacrifice the utilization of the maintenance force at certain times in order to have them available as needed at critical periods. (Note, it may be possible to reduce low utilization periods by using outside serv-

ices at peak demand levels.) In effect we can conclude that keeping equipment operating will tend to be the major factor and maintenance personnel utilization the minor factor. Therefore, since the major factor requires some sacrifice on the part of the minor factor—maintenance personnel utilization may be relatively low in order to raise product equipment utilization.

However, although maintenance personnel utilization may need to be sacrificed in order to minimize total cost it is necessary to maintain maximum levels of maintenance personnel effectiveness and efficiency when they are on job assignments. Maximization of effectiveness does not conflict with sacrifice of utilization. Utilization is the ratio of time worked to time available for work. It is in effect a measure of idleness since (1 − level of utilization) = idleness level. Effectiveness or efficiency during periods of activity is not involved. In order to measure effectiveness some measure of the quality of the work performed must be established. There will also be a close relationship between effectiveness and efficency. Efficiency can be defined as a measure of how well the maintenance personnel perform against an established standard for measuring output. The most satisfactory measure of output of labor is the standard hour. If we establish a standard time for the job then we can measure performance against standard which is a measure of efficiency, *e.g.*,

$$\text{Efficiency} = \frac{\text{Output}}{\text{Input}} = \frac{\text{Standard hours earned}}{\text{Hours worked against standard}} = \text{Performance.}$$

FIGURE 10–3

Maintenance Job Ticket

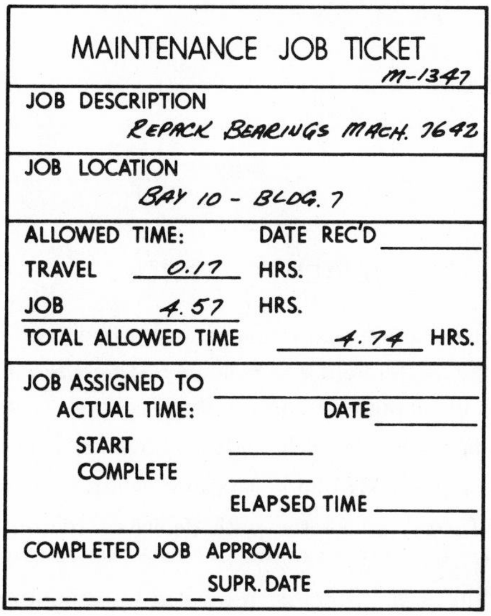
MAINTENANCE JOB TICKET
M-1347
JOB DESCRIPTION
REPACK BEARINGS MACH. 7642
JOB LOCATION
BAY 10 - BLDG. 7
ALLOWED TIME: DATE REC'D ______
TRAVEL 0.17 HRS.
JOB 4.57 HRS.
TOTAL ALLOWED TIME 4.74 HRS.
JOB ASSIGNED TO ______
ACTUAL TIME: DATE ______
START ______
COMPLETE ______
ELAPSED TIME ______
COMPLETED JOB APPROVAL
SUPR. DATE ______

This says that if we establish standard hours for maintenance jobs and then maintain records of actual time on the job for any individual, group, or function we can obtain a measure of efficiency by comparing the actual time spent to the standard time allowed. Note that only time for jobs assigned are considered—not idle time when unassigned.

The simplest method to obtain necessary performance data is a simple job ticket as illustrated in Figure 10–3. Although a manual ticket is illustrated it is readily adaptable to electronic data processing form.

Although times for maintenance operations are more variable than for production or routine jobs, standard times have been established and successfully used by a number of progressive firms. Measures of efficiency on individual jobs must recognize the limitation of basing standards on average content, but if weekly or monthly performance indexes are established this variation is minimized and control meaningful. See Figure 10–4.

FIGURE 10–4

Maintenance Performance Record and Report

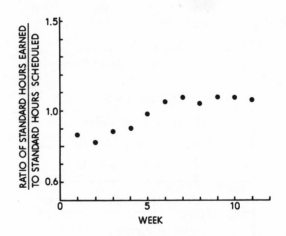

REVIEW QUESTIONS

1. Distinguish between failure maintenance and preventive maintenance.
2. What is meant by maintenance efficiency? How does this differ from the concept of efficiency as normally used in production?
3. Explain the significance of the schematic diagram in Figure 10–1.
4. Name and briefly explain six major decisions relative to maintenance.
5. Discuss the cost factors associated with decisions relating to use of external or internal service staffs.
6. List and discuss the basic principles involved in evaluating decisions relating to equipment replacement.

7. How is the replacement parts inventory problem similar to the production parts problem? How does it differ?

8. Distinguish between maintenance effectiveness and maintenance personnel efficiency.

PROBLEMS

1. Given: $P(F) = \dfrac{e^{-\lambda}\lambda^x}{x!}$, where λ is the mean man-hours of preventive maintenance per time period and x is the random variable, hours of preventive maintenance.

   $C_F = 50^{\lambda/10}$, measured in dollars.

   Cost per man-hour of preventive maintenance = \$10.

   Find: Optimum man-hours of preventive maintenance per time period.

2. Assume a firm has a policy of reviewing and replenishing spare parts inventory on the first of each month (assume as a 21-day work period). A particular item in inventory costs \$30 each. Annual holding cost is 25 percent of inventory value and the cost of not having a spare part on hand when needed is \$20 per hour. If it requires 5 days to order and receive the part and the firm works a single 8-hour shift per day, what is the desired beginning-of-month inventory level? Weekly demand is normally distributed with a mean of 4 and variance of 0.49.

3. During a production month, the plant maintenance department paid maintenance personnel for 3,870 man hours of labor. Eighty percent of the work assigned had standards established for a total of 2,860 standard hours which was accomplished in 2,570 man hours. What was the (a) utilization of the maintenance staff, (b) performance of the maintenance staff? Would you recommend any factors for management to audit?

Chapter 11

PLANNING AND ORGANIZING THE MAINTENANCE FUNCTION

PERHAPS ONE of the first questions likely to arise in organizing for maintenance is the question of assignment of personnel to preventive v. emergency maintenance. In general, if the same group is used for both functions, some time must be allocated during scheduling for unforeseen breakdowns. If the allocated time is excessive to emergency requirements, maintenance personnel utilization drops. If insufficient time is allocated for emergencies, preventive maintenance is delayed until emergencies are taken care of. If this last occurs frequently it is likely to lead to inadequate preventive maintenance which in turn can lead to excessive emergency demands which at the extreme may tend to completely eliminate the preventive program. The solution is not to allocate average time required for emergency maintenance since by statistics we know that insufficient time will be provided 50 percent of the time.

If separate divisions are established for preventive and for emergency maintenance it is possible to maintain a reasonably high utilization of those personnel assigned to preventive maintenance by use of planned maintenance operation sequences and standard times for maintenance operations. The problem is then reduced to one of staffing optimally for emergency maintenance. If the same personnel are used for both preventive and emergency maintenance we can apply the same manpower planning principle by establishing the staffing required for preventive maintenance and then superimposing upon this the optimum additional staff required for emergency maintenance. Although in principle this appears reasonable, the establishment of optimum may be difficult even after agreement upon criteria for determination of optimum. We do, however, have means of

162

objectively analyzing segments of the total problem which if applied individually in a systematic manner will permit a closer approach to optimality for the total maintenance program.

These segments of the total maintenance program which may be handled in an objective manner include:

   a) Selection of preventive maintenance activities or operations.
   b) Determination of preventive maintenance operation frequency.
   c) Repair or replace decisions.
   d) Staffing the maintenance function.
   e) Scheduling maintenance activities.
   f) Follow up and control of maintenance activities.

SELECTION OF PREVENTIVE MAINTENANCE ACTIVITIES OR OPERATIONS

The objective of any preventive maintenance program is to reduce the total cost of providing a service. In order to determine the effectiveness of a preventive maintenance program it is necessary to compare costs of the program with those costs which would occur if no preventive maintenance were practiced. In order to accomplish this objectively, knowledge must be available relative to:

1. Frequency of failure.
2. Cause of failure.
3. Cost of failure (includes repair, lost production, goodwill, and so forth).
4. Cost of preventive maintenance to reduce or eliminate the cause of failure.

If C_b is the cost of a breakdown and C_p the cost of preventive maintenance then preventive maintenance is economical if:

$$C_p < C_b$$

To determine the expected cost of breakdown per period if there is no preventive maintenance we divide the cost of breakdown, C_b, by the expected number of periods between breakdowns, $E(n) = \sum_n p_n n$, where n is the period, and p_n the probability of failure in period n. This results in expected period maintenance total cost, $(TC) = \dfrac{C_b}{E(n)}$, when there is no preventive maintenance. For example, assume the following probability distribution for failure:

n^{th} Period after Maintenance	p_n	$p_n n$
1	0.1	0.1
2	0.2	0.4
3	0.4	1.2
4	0.3	1.2
		$\sum_n p_n n = 2.9$

Then $(TC) = \left(\dfrac{C_b}{2.9}\right)$ with no preventive maintenance. Note that in a real world situation rather than assuming no preventive maintenance we can start with present maintenance program and costs, establishing expected period total costs for present maintenance policy and consider this as our base for analysis. Knowing C_b, the economics of alternative policies can be analyzed.

DETERMINATION OF PREVENTIVE MAINTENANCE FREQUENCY

The expected period cost without preventive maintenance has been established above. We now desire to determine the optimum period frequency for preventive maintenance. We do this by finding expected period costs for policies of successively increasing periods between maintenance until the minimum point on the total cost curve has been determined. To illustrate, assume that a breakdown in the case above costs $100. Then, expected period cost, no preventive maintenance equals:

$$(TC) = \frac{C_b}{E(n)} = \frac{\$100}{2.9} = \$34.48.$$

If the preventive maintenance costs $C_p = \$15$ to perform and it is performed each period then the expected period cost is $15 for the preventive maintenance plus the expected cost of failure between preventive maintenance operations or, expected total cost, one-period policy equals:

$$C_p + C_b(p_1) = \$15 + \$100\,(0.1) = \$25.$$

For a two-period policy the average period cost of preventive maintenance equals $C_p/2$, but failure may have occurred during either the first or second period, plus if it failed during the first period, there is a possibility an additional failure also occurred during the second period. If we call the first period expected failure F_1, then the probability of another failure the second month is $F_1 p_1$. Combining, expected period total cost, two-period policy equals:

$$1/2[C_p + C_b(p_1 + p_2) + (F_1 p_1)C_b] =$$
$$1/2[\$15 + \$100(0.1 + 0.2) + [(0.1)(0.1)]\$100] =$$
$$1/2[\$15 + \$30 + \$1] = \$23.$$

In general, if F_n is the total expected failure rate for period n, expected period cost under an n-period policy equals:

$$1/n[C_p + C_b F_n]$$

where,

$$F_n = p_1 + p_2 + \cdots + p_n + F_1 p_{n-1} + F_2 p_{n-2} + \cdots + F_{n-1} p_1$$

Applying the preceding formulas to the example provides the following data:

End of Period n Policy	Expected Period Cost
0 (no preventive maintenance)	$34.48
1	25.00
2	23.00
3	30.14
4	33.18

For the case above, the optimum maintenance policy is to provide preventive maintenance at the end of each second period resulting in an expected period cost of $23. Note that the above has been determined for a single piece of equipment. To estimate cost for N units merely multiply the single piece of equipment cost by N.

REPAIR VERSUS REPLACE DECISIONS

Before beginning the discussion of repair versus replace decisions, it is pointed out that in those cases where failure is complete (*e.g.*, no repair possible after failure, such as light bulbs), the question reduces to one of periodic total quantity replacement or failure replacement, and the analysis is quite similar to that above for preventive maintenance programming. Note that in fact four type policies are possible:

a) Replace all (both good and failed units) periodically.
b) Replace only failed units periodically.
c) Replace only failed units as they fail.
d) Replace failed units as they fail and also replace both good and bad periodically.

If we select policy (*d*) and the cost of replacing an item periodically is C_p and of replacing a failed item as it fails is C_b, the expected period costs are identical to those determined previously for alternative preventive maintenance programs. Policy (*c*) results in an expected cost equal to the expected cost of no preventive maintenance as stated.

Policy (*a*) demands that the period between replacements be as extensive as possible without reducing the system performance level below minimum acceptable levels. For example, if minimum allowed lighting levels were 70 percent of maximum lighting levels, using the data in the example above we would replace all bulbs at the end of two periods since we would expect the lighting level to drop to 70 percent $(1 - (0.1 + 0.2))$ of maximum at that time. To replace at the end of one period would double the cost and if we waited longer than two periods the lighting level would drop below the acceptable minimum.

For policy (*b*) the objective is to determine the optimum replacement schedule for failed units. Using the example previously given where we replace at the end of each period, there will be failures of those items installed during previous periods, or expected failures $= F_n$. Therefore, expected period cost for a one-period policy equals $(C_b F_n)$. Note that if it is desired to determine cost when the replacement period equals two of the periods above, the probabilities between replacements are the sums of each exclusive sequenced pairs of the original periods. If F_n' is the longer period expected failures then total cost per replacement period $= (C_b F_n')$ and in terms of original period's expected cost $\frac{1}{n}(C_b F_n')$.

REPLACEMENT POLICIES

Replacement models have been covered fully in *The Capacity Decision System* of this series. However, replacement and maintenance are inseparable. As a result we look at industry practice and some basic guides.

A survey of replacement practices in a sample of industry[1] indicates that 56 percent of the companies surveyed had no special replacement policy and an additional 23 percent had no written policy. Stated differently, only 21 percent of industry has a written standard policy for equipment replacement. Other significant results of the survey indicate that payback in years (40 percent) and rate of return (32 percent) are the most popular decision basis. Also, although division managers, general managers, chief engineers, superintendents, or department heads make 78 percent of the recommendations, the final decision rests at or above the vice presidential level in 79 percent of the firms. Of the firms surveyed 42 percent maintained historical records on all machines and 18 percent on no machines.

These survey results indicate that replacement is considered a critical decision—hence high-level, historical data is most often not available, and simple decision rules are desired. Another inherent characteristic implied is that forecast of life, depreciation, and operating costs are difficult. If this last were not true routine decision processes could be established and decision assigned as lower organizational responsibilities. The problems of forecasting will not be covered here, but, assuming forecasts are adequate, the following rules and techniques apply to the stated decision criteria.

1. *General Rule.* Replace at the end of any period if ownership, operation, and maintenance costs of the next period exceed the average cost through the period preceding replacement. This assumes that the sum of period costs are nondecreasing. Symbolically the optimum period's life, n^*, satisfies the relationship,

$$\frac{\sum\limits_{i=1}^{n-1}(TC_i)}{n-1} \leq \frac{\sum\limits_{i=1}^{n}(TC_i)}{n} < \frac{\sum\limits_{i=1}^{n+1}(TC_i)}{n+1}$$

where (TC_i) is the total cost of period i of ownership, operation, and maintenance.

---

[1] R. G. Murdick, "Equipment Replacement Practices," *Automation* (November, 1965), p. 121.

2. Repair the Existing Facility or Replace with Facility of Equivalent capability. In this instance the criteria as before is to minimize period cost but the useful life of the existing facility and the replacement may not be equal. It is therefore necessary to assume that each alternative will be replaced as necessary at the end of its useful life by identical equipment until the total time period for each is equal to the total time period of the other. This total time may be either finite or infinite. If we now let:

I = Initial investment
TC_n = Total cost over n periods
C_j = Period operating and maintenance costs
i = Rate of return
P = Equivalent present worth
S_n = Salvage value at the end of n periods

then,

$$P = I + \sum_{j=1}^{n} \frac{C_j}{(1+i)^j} - \frac{S_n}{(1+i)^n}$$

for a useful life of n periods. Furthermore, if the asset is replaced k times, the total period is kn and the present worth for kn periods is:

$$P = \left[I + \sum_{j=1}^{n} \frac{C_j}{(1+i)^j} - \frac{S_n}{(1+i)^n} \right] \left[1 + \sum_{}^{k-1} \frac{1}{(1+i)^n} \right].$$

Equivalent present worths can now be established knowing I and C_j for each alternative. Note that I for the present facility I_p is the net realizable value plus repair cost or:

I_p = Net realizable market value plus repair cost
     = Market value minus removal cost plus repair cost

and I_c the initial cost of the challenging replacement is equal to installed cost. Useful life of each should be determined at optimum as noted previously in (1). Note further that for a finite period for kn, the equivalent annual cost, EAC, considering the time value of money is:

$$EAC = P \left[\frac{i(1+i)^{kn}}{(1+i)^{kn} - 1} \right]$$

and for an infinite life,

$$EAC = (Pi).$$

3. An Improved Design Facility Considered as a Replacement for the Present Facility. An improved design normally represents either the ability to perform the required function at lower cost or increased capacity for the function over the present facility. If the increased capacity is not required either at present or in the planned future, then both facilities satisfy the reqirements and the decision should be made under the assumption of equivalent capability as in rule 2. However, if the increased capacity or capability is not required at present but will be required in the future the decision becomes one of when to replace, since at some future time it will become economically desirable to have the added capability (capacity).

The period cost of the existing machine at some time in the future must now include the cost of lost opportunity due to its failure to have the added capability of the replacement which we represent by C_{oj} for the jth period. Then, by our general rule, when the cost of an additional period for present equipment exceeds the average period cost of the replacement we should replace. If N is the replacement period then:

$$C_N + C_{oN} + S_{N-1}(1+i) - S_N \leq EAC \text{ of replacement}$$
$$\leq C_{N+1} + C_{o, N+1} + S_N(1+i) - S_{N+1}.$$

Note that the principle of sunk cost is inherent in the above decision rule, in that only salvage values (net realizable) are considered. If, when the decision is between repair or replace the cost of repair exceeds the increase in salvage value due to repair, the difference between repair cost and added salvage value must be considered a cost for the year in which it occurs. This is provided for by including the repair cost as a portion of that year's operation and maintenance costs and adding to the salvage value of that year the increase in net realizable value due to the repair. The significance of this is that if major overhaul is necessary without adding materially to the net realizable value of the facility, economics of the situations may dictate replacement. It is the failure to objectively analyze the economics on other than initial cost when considering repair or replacement which often results in retention of equipment past its economic life.

STAFFING THE MAINTENANCE FUNCTION

Effective staffing of the maintenance function is dependent upon the ability of the maintenance organization to handle both preventive and emergency (breakdown) requirements. One advantage of preventive maintenance is that the maintenance can be scheduled. Although the operation time variance will be greater for maintenance than production operations, if the maintenance operation is defined and time standards established manpower requirements and job assignments for men or crews can be determined rather readily. In scheduling jobs for a production man or crew the objective is to assign individual tasks until the sum of task times equals the available work time. Setup or changeover times are scheduled between jobs. The same principle applies to preventive maintenance assignments. If period to period total requirements are balanced, a satisfactory balance and utilization of personnel and equipment can be maintained. Techniques such as Gantt charting, network analysis, sequencing, and linear programming may be used in the same manner as for production operations, making the necessary allowance for travel between jobs (changeover) and increased variance for operation times.

Emergency maintenance staffing presents a more difficult problem due to the random characteristic of failure occurrence. It is necessary in this case to establish maintenance staffing which will result in optimum cost. To optimize cost of emergency maintenance, a balance must be sought between the cost of maintenance staffing and the cost of facility downtime.

If sufficient historical data is available or if samples can be obtained which adequately define the stochastic characteristics of input variables, and if these stochastic characteristics adequately follow certain known distributions, analytical models may be used which satisfactorily simulate the operating characteristics of the emergency maintenance function and optimum levels may be established. If distributions do not satisfy known analytical model requirements Monte Carlo simulation methods may be used to estimate optimums.

To illustrate the use of analytical models let us assume that equipment fails such that the probability that exactly x units fail in time t can be approximated by the Poisson distribution:

$$f(x,t) = \frac{e^{-\lambda t}(\lambda t)^x}{x!}.$$

Note that the mean of the distribution is λt, the mean failures in time t. The mean rate at which equipment fails is then:

$$\frac{\lambda t}{t} = \lambda.$$

Machines are serviced in the order in which they fail (FIFO), and the time for service by a crew of fixed size is a random variable z, following a negative exponential distribution such that:

$$g(z) = \mu e^{-\mu z}$$

such that μ is the mean rate of service.

If there are N machines which may require service and k service crews it can be shown that:

1. The probability of no machines waiting for or being serviced is,

$$p_o = 1 - \sum_{n=1}^{N} p_n.$$

2. The probability of n machines waiting for or being serviced,

$$p_n = \frac{N!}{n!(N-n)!}\left(\frac{\lambda}{\mu}\right)^n p_o, \, o \leq n < k$$

$$p_n = \frac{N!}{(N-n)!k!k^{(n-k)}}\left(\frac{\lambda}{\mu}\right)^n p_o, \, k \leq n \leq N.$$

3. (1) and (2) result in

$$P_o = \cfrac{1}{\displaystyle\sum_{n=o}^{k-1} \frac{N!}{n!(N-n)!}\left(\frac{\lambda}{\mu}\right)^n + \sum_{n=k}^{N} \frac{N!}{(N-n)!k!k^{(n-k)}}\left(\frac{\lambda}{\mu}\right)^n}.$$

4. The expected number of machines waiting for service or being serviced is:

$$E(n) = \sum_{n=o}^{N} np_n.$$

Now, note that if the expected number of machines being or awaiting service is $E(n)$ the expected hourly cost of machine downtime, C_d, is [$E(n)$ · cost per hour downtime per machine], and the hourly cost of maintenance personnel, C_m, is [k · hourly maintenance labor rate · (crew size)] or total cost, $TC = C_d + C_m$. The optimum number of crews, k^*, to assign to serve N machines can be determined by finding k which minimizes TC.

For example, assume there are six machines with Poisson failures at mean rate λ, and a maintenance service man can service at the mean rate μ, with service time distributed as a negative exponential, and $\dfrac{\lambda}{\mu} = 0.1$. It is desired to determine the number of maintenance men to assign if downtime costs \$32 per hour and maintenance labor, including fringes, costs \$5 per hour. The resultant probabilistic calculations are:

n	p_n $k=1$	p_n $k=2$	p_n $k=3$
0	0.4845	0.5688	0.5702
1	0.2907	0.3413	0.3421
2	0.1454	0.0853	0.0855
3	0.0582	0.0028	0.0011
4	0.0175	0.0013	0.0001
5	0.0035	0.0003	0.0001
6	0.0003	0.0001	0

For,

$$k=1, E(n) = \sum_{n=o}^{6} np_n = 1(0.2907) + 2(0.1454) + 3(0.0582) + 4(0.0175)$$
$$+ 5(0.0035) + 6(0.0003) = 0.7454$$

$$k=2, E(n) = \sum_{n=o}^{6} np_n = 1(0.3413) + 2(0.0853) + 3(0.0028) + 4(0.0013)$$
$$+ 5(0.0003) + 6(0.0001) = 0.5276$$

$$k=3, E(n) = \sum_{n=o}^{6} np_n = 1(0.3421) + 2(0.0855) + 3(0.0011) + 4(0.0001)$$
$$+ 5(0.0001) + 6(0) = 0.5173$$

$$TC = C_d + C_m =$$

$k = 1$, $TC = (0.7454)($32$) + 1($5$) = 28.85 per hour
$k = 2$, $TC = (0.5276)($32$) + 2($5$) = 26.88 per hour
$k = 3$, $TC = (0.5173)($32$) + 3($5$) = 31.55 per hour

resulting in $k^* = 2$ maintenance men at an average hourly total cost of $26.88.

Before using the formulas above tests should be run to assure satisfactory conformity to the arrival and service distributions. When conformity is unsatisfactory Monte Carlo simulation should be used. Note also that the above relationships do not resolve the question of the optimum number of machines to assign to a fixed crew size. This is a combinatorial problem, probably, as conveniently handled by Monte Carlo as by any other means.

Except in relatively simple cases, analysis by hand is time consuming and subject to arithmetic errors. It is therefore desirable to utilize a computer for analytic or Monte Carlo solutions for most problems of this type.

SCHEDULING MAINTENANCE ACTIVITIES

In order to schedule it is necessary that (1) the jobs to be performed be defined and (2) an estimate, as accurate as reasonable, of time required to perform the job be available. This may be, and usually is, difficult in advance for breakdown or failure repair due to the inability to predict a breakdown occurrence and the difficulty in prior establishment of repair operations necessary to return the equipment to the line. However, although subject to relatively high variance, standards may be established for failure types and over the long run will provide a measurement of efficiency of crews while on assignment. Proper staffing may be the more important consideration for emergency maintenance personnel. Preventive maintenance operations, including routine repairs and equipment shutdowns or overhauls, may be scheduled effectively since definition of operations is possible and reasonable standard times can be established. We therefore limit our discussion primarily to these later operations.

In planning and scheduling maintenance either manual or electronic data processing systems are feasible. Since the principles and outputs for each are the same we use the manual system to illustrate.

Three records or outputs are the minimum required for a maintenance planning system:

1. Equipment history card.
2. Maintenance route list and schedule.
3. Maintenance job order.

The equipment history card,

   a) Defines the operations to be performed on the unit equipment.
   b) Notes inspection frequency.

   c) Notes state of equipment during inspection.
   d) Records dates and personnel who perform inspections.

A sample history card is shown in Figure 11–1.

FIGURE 11–1
Equipment History Card

CARD NO.	EQUIPMENT CODE: *DCMO* NO. *053*	COST CENTER 14	EQUIPMENT HISTORY CARD	EQUIPMENT NAME: *DC MOTOR*			
INSPECTION POINT		RUNNING OR DOWN	FREQ.	DATE	POINTS	INSP. BY	REMARKS
1 BEARINGS		*R D*	*W A*	*2/6/--*	*1, 4, 5*	*170642*	
2 ALIGNMENT		*R*	*W*				
3 BRUSHES		*D*	*SA*				
4 COMMUTATOR		*D*	*Q*				
5 WINDINGS		*D*	*M*				

   The maintenance route list is prepared for either daily or weekly job assignments, listing in sequence the jobs to be performed by the individual or crew. A standard routing may be established depending upon the combination of daily, weekly, monthly, quarterly, semiannual, and annual maintenance to be performed. If a computer is used in scheduling it is easier to balance loads between schedule periods and between maintenance personnel during periods. A sample route sheet is shown in Figure 11–2.

FIGURE 11–2
Maintenance Route Sheet

MAINTENANCE ROUTE SHEET					
FOR _____ ASSIGNED TO_____ BY *D. H (FOREMAN)*					
EQUIPMENT NAME	NO.	OPERATIONS	STD. TIME (MINS.)	COST CENTER	REMARKS
D.C. MOTOR	*053*	*BEARINGS*			
		COMMUTATORS			
		WINDINGS	*86*	*14*	
TOTAL TIME			*448*		

The maintenance route sheet may serve as the job tickets for those jobs listed or individual job orders may be attached. If EDP is used it may be desired to prepare an individual card for each job which may be completed by the operator using either mark sense or port-a-punch. This can then be used to control against both the maintenance route sheet listing and the equipment history card. These controls must also be established in the manual system but the separate job order may not be necessary, or desired, due to increased processing complexity.

Even though a separate job order may not be used for the operations on the route sheet, they are necessary for emergency work assignments or special inspection requests received by the maintenance department. A sample is shown in Figure 11–3.

FIGURE 11–3

Maintenance Job Order

	DATE WANTED	DATE SCHEDULED	COST CENTER	EQUIP.CODE.	EQUIP. NO.	ACCT. NO.	EMERGENCY	
ITTEN '30/65	6/8/65	6/8/65	60	MOD	052	11	YES	NO ✓

MAINTENANCE JOB ORDER   NO. 74643

IPMENT NAME   DEPT. LOCATION
D.C. MOTOR

K TO BE DONE
CLEAN MOTOR, CLEAN COMMUTATOR,
REPLACE BRUSHES & SEAT AS REQUIRED.

SHUT DOWN   YES ✓   NO

SHUT DOWN DATE

WHAT MUST BE DOWN   MACH. ✓   DEPT. ☐

JESTED BY	APPROVED BY	M.W.	WELD	ELEC.	SHOP	PIPE	CARP	PAINT	P.C.	OIL	INST.	YARD			
		1	2	(3)	4	5	6	7	8	9	10	11			

	NAME	DATE	JOB COST SUMMARY		
	ASSIGNED TO J.D.	6/8		EST	ACT	VAR
RK DONE			LABOR HRS. /		
	COMPLETED BY		LABOR COST 6.60		
	INSPECTED BY		SUPPLIES & PARTS COST 9.00		
	ACCEPTED BY		TOTAL 15.60		

FOLLOW–UP AND CONTROL OF MAINTENANCE ACTIVITIES

Follow-up and control is primarily concerned with the determination of the effectiveness of the maintenance activity. Basically effectiveness must be measured on the basis of facility availability and the utilization of maintenance personnel.

Utilization of maintenance personnel is measured by maintaining a satisfactory active time to idle time ratio and control of labor performance during the active time.

1. *Work Time versus Idle Time.* As we have seen above it is normally not economical to have maintenance personnel occupied 100 percent of the time. In order to accomplish 100 percent utilization excessive postponement of critical maintenance will be necessary which will raise the total cost. However, preventive maintenance labor can be scheduled to require reasonably high activity levels. Even emergency maintenance personnel when considered as a group should maintain a rather consistent activity level although lower than preventive personnel. The level of activity can be measured by work sampling. This measure is less meaningful, however, than control of labor performance.

2. *Control of labor performance.* Labor performance can be measured if a standard time system has been established. Over some basic time measurement period (day, week, month) summaries of standard hours scheduled and standard hours earned can be obtained. From these

$$\text{Period performance} = \frac{\text{Standard hours earned}}{\text{Hours worked against standard}} = \text{Labor efficiency.}$$

By maintaining a line graph of period performance for an extended period trends and variations can be noted and evaluated and corrective action as necessary initiated.

Other measures which may be effectively used include (*a*) a line graph report of the ratio of standard hours earned to total hours paid which measures the effectiveness of staffing and (*b*) a line graph report of cost of materials and supplies per standard hour earned which measures material usage.

FIGURE 11-4

Maintenance Cost versus Utilization

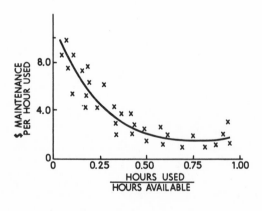

None of these ratios have universally meaningful target levels. Each organization will find levels which can be maintained and which reflect satisfactory operating levels for their peculiar conditions.

3. *Utilization of Equipment or Equipment Availability.* This may be a more difficult problem to measure adequately than labor performance. Utilization may need to be measured by unit of equipment, equipment type, responsibility, or combinations of the three. The basic data required is (*a*) hours available and (*b*) hours used. Hours used, in particular, must be measured accurately with the measurement being independent of any operator or supervisor bias. Utilization is, then, the ratio of hours used to hours available. The improvement of utilization may be through joint efforts of maintenance and production.

An effective means of measuring and controlling overall cost is to plot "dollars for maintenance per hour equipment used" versus "utilization." A sample for fork trucks is shown in Figure 11–4. The regression line in this case is "eyeballed," which is usually satisfactory. If deemed necessary a regression equation could be determined mathematically.

Having established the cost to use relationship the objective is to combine low utilization-high cost equipment to raise utilization and reduce use-hour cost. To estimate the effect of combinations use may be made of the analysis form of Figure 11–5.

FIGURE 11–5

Maintenance Cost by Use-Hour Analysis

MAINTENANCE COST BY USE=HOUR ANALYSIS								
Initial Data (1 year—2000 hrs.)						*Analysis*		
Equip. No.	*$ Maint.*	*Hrs. Used*	*$ Maint./ per Hr. Used*	*Combined with Equip. No.*	*Combined Hrs. Use (1)*	*$ Maint./ per Hr. Used (2)*	*Est'd $ Maint. (3) = (1)(2)*	*Savings*
24	1236	210	$5.89	27 and 18	627	$3.25 from appropriate curve at 627 hrs. use	$2037.75	$1692.43
27	1370	221	$6.20	. . . .				
18	1124	196	$5.73	. . . .				

NOTE: Unless the excess equipment is disposed of no savings result. Shutdown does not eliminate but in fact may increase total cost. For example, from the data of Figure 11–5, trucks number 24 and 27 should be disposed of.

MAINTENANCE SIMULATION BY MONTE CARLO

Monte Carlo is based upon sampling theory and as a result lends itself to the solution of any problem where distributional patterns of individual or combined factors can be developed. The minimum requirements for solution are distributional data of the affecting factors and a table of random numbers. To illustrate, let us assume the following conditions:

A company has 10 machines producing a semifinished good which is then processed by mechanical conveyor through five manual operations. The company has not felt it practical to establish a reserve stock between the machine and the line. As a result, the stoppage of the machine or conveyor line tends to result in the other being stopped for an equal time. Maintenance logs indi-

FIGURE 11–6   FIGURE 11–7

Machine Running Time between   Maintenance Time per Machine
Stoppages   Stoppage

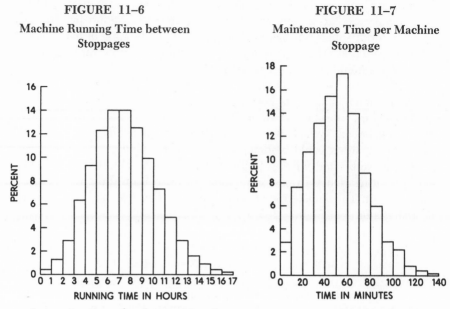

cate running times for the machines between stoppages are distributed as indicated in Figure 11–6. The time required to get the equipment operating again is indicated in Figure 11–7. Similar data for the conveyor system are given in Figures 11–8 and 11–9. In addition, the machine requires reload every two hours. Reload requires 10 to 15 minutes. As a result, practice is to allow the persons on the line a 15-minute rest break at these times while the operator reloads.

The question has arisen as to the number of maintenance men to assign to the machines. It has been decided that machine operator plus line operator costs represent the cost of idle time. This is justified on the basis that hours of work are dependent upon orders for goods. Machine times are fixed by output re-

FIGURE 11–8   FIGURE 11–9

Conveyor Running Time between   Maintenance Time per
Stoppages   Conveyor Stoppage

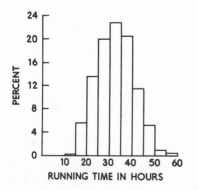

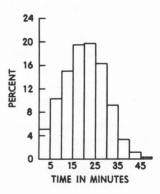

quirements and labor time is equal to machine time plus idle time. Therefore, reduction of idle time will reduce labor time by an equal amount, but machine time and its related costs will be unaffected.

Labor costs are line operators, $1.40 per hour; machine operator, $1.90 per hour; maintenance man, $2.25 per hour.

Procedure for Analysis

1. Prepare frequency distribution histograms or tables. (Histograms are shown in Figures 11–6 through 11–9.)
2. Prepare cumulative distribution curves for the frequency distributions (shown in Figures 11–10 and 11–11). Note that these do not have to conform to one of the mathematically expressible distribution curves. The important consideration is that enough samples be taken to assure stability and reliability of the curve.
3. Select random times for first reload. (In the illustration three-digit random numbers lower than 120 were used to represent minutes.)
4. Determine initial machine running times.
   a) Random number tables are rectangular distributions signifying that any number has the same probability of occurring as any other number.
   b) If two-place random numbers are assumed to represent probability, we can take random numbers from the tables in some assigned sequence, use the random number to enter the appropriate curve

FIGURE 11–10

Cumulative Curves for Machines

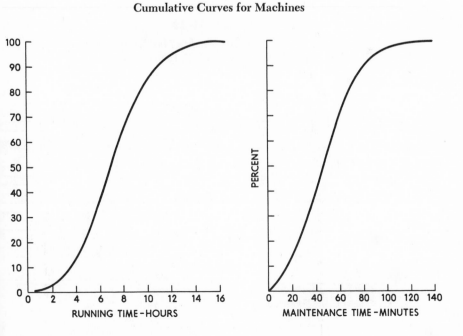

FIGURE 11–11

Cumulative Curves for Conveyors

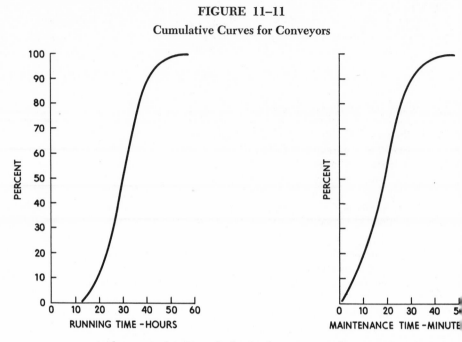

on the vertical axis, and obtain the corresponding running time on the horizontal axis for each of the machines.

5. Determine initial conveyor line running times in the same manner. To assure random relationships between times, follow a different path in

FIGURE 11–12

Gantt Chart of One Maintenance Man for 10 Units

(Idle Time for 80-Hour Study—42 Hours, 55 Minutes)

MACHINE				
1	71	23 4.9	64 33	
2	83	05 2.7	10 20	
3	07	14 4.0	71 34	
4	17	38 6.1	60 32	
5	63	97 12.9	37 27	
6	92	11 3.7	47 29	
7	48	43 6.3	38 27	
8	43	93 11.2	73 35	
9	76	72 6.7	32 26	
10	90	61 5.9	97 46	

TIME BEFORE RELOAD – MINUTES | MACHINE RUNNING TIME–HOURS | CONVEYOR RUNNING TIME–HOURS

HOURS   1   2   3   4   5   10   15

☐ RUNNING   ▨ RELOAD

▧ MAINTENANCE   ▨ IDLE (WAIT)

the random number table or use a different table. (In the illustration four separate tables were used.)

6. Plot derived times on Gantt chart until first stoppage occurs.
7. Determine earliest stoppage.
8. Using random number tables and curve determine maintenance time and plot on Gantt chart.
9. Determine next earliest stoppage and repeat step 8.

   a) If the maintenance man is still occupied on previous machine stoppage, he is delayed until the earlier stoppage is corrected. This creates idle time which would be avoidable if free maintenance personnel were available.

   b) If idle time occurs, plot on Gantt chart delaying maintenance until personnel is available.

10. Continue for predetermined period or until ratio of total idle time to total machine time tends to remain constant.

    Note: Method accuracy improves roughly as $\sqrt{N}$ where N is the number of trials.

11. Determine total cost.
12. Repeat steps 6 through 11 for additional numbers of maintenance personnel until minimum total cost is determined.

In the illustration it was not necessary to continue with more than two maintenance men since the cost of idle time with two men is less than the cost of a third man. This is illustrated in Figure 11–13.

FIGURE 11–13

80-Hour Cost Analysis

No. of Maintenance Men	Maintenance Cost	Idle Time		Total Cost
		Hours	*Cost*	
1	$180.00	42.9	$381.81	$561.81
2	$360.00	3.96	$ 35.24	$395.24

Conclusions:
1. Optimum solution is to use two maintenance men.
2. Third man would cost more than total idle time cost with two men.
3. Cost savings by using two men rather than one man is approximately $166.57 per 80-hour period.

REVIEW QUESTIONS

1. Discuss the nature of the problem of distributing preventive and failure maintenance assignments among maintenance department personnel.
2. Name and explain some factors influencing the selection of preventive maintenance operations.
3. What alternative policies are available when the question of repair or replacement of equipment arises?
4. What is the general rule for deciding when to replace equipment?

5. Why is it easier to schedule preventive than failure maintenance activities? How does this affect organization of the maintenance function?

6. What criteria should determine the decision between selection of an analytical model or a Monte Carlo simulation for determination of staffing levels for maintenance?

7. What are the three records required for a maintenance planning system and what purpose does each record serve?

8. Why is "dollars for maintenance per hour equipment used" rather than "maintenance dollars for equipment" used in Figure 11–4?

9. What is the basis for Monte Carlo simulation?

10. What decision criteria is used when applying Monte Carlo to maintenance staffing problems? What parameters might be varied in analyzing the problem?

PROBLEMS

1. If it requires 6 hours at $10 per hour to perform a certain preventive maintenance operation which avoids a breakdown costing $125, how often should preventive maintenance be performed if the following probabilities of failure in period after maintenance have been estimated from historical records?

Period after Preventive Maintenance	Relative Frequency of Failure
1	.06
2	.11
3	.18
4	.27
5	.17
6	.17
7	.04

2. In an office area it is desirable to keep lighting levels above 80 percent of maximum. In the office there are 360 bulbs which cost $1.68 each. It costs the company $15 to have a maintenance man visit the office (preparation and travel cost) plus an average of $0.24 for each bulb replaced for direct labor effort. What policy would you recommend if bulb life has a normal distribution with a mean of 2000 hours and standard deviation of 75 hours?

3. *a)* If a firm has 8 maintenance men assigned to service 120 machines which tend to fail in Poisson manner with mean time between failures of 2 hours, and it requires an average of 5 minutes' service time for one man (service time has a negative exponential distribution) per breakdown what would be the average number of machines awaiting service?

   b) If a machine being down costs $40 per hour and maintenance labor costs $10 per hour, would you recommend changing the maintenance crew size? Why?

BIBLIOGRAPHY

BIBLIOGRAPHY

ABRUZZI, ADAM, "Developing Standard Data for Predictive Purposes," *Journal of Industrial Engineering*, Vol. 2, No. 3 (November, 1952), p. 15.

ABRUZZI, ADAM, *Work Measurement—New Principles and Procedures*. New York: Columbia University Press, 1952.

"A Hard Boiled Look at Your Plant's Home Town," *Factory*, Vol. 123, No. 5 (May, 1961), p. 180.

APPLE, JAMES M., *Plant Layout and Materials Handling*. New York: The Ronald Press Co., 1950.

ARIES, ROBERT S., "Methods of Determining Plant Location," *Chemical Engineering Progress*, Vol. 45, No. 5 (May, 1949), p. 285.

ARKIN, H., AND R. R. COLTON, *Statistical Methods*. New York: Barnes & Noble, Inc., 1939.

ARMOUR, G. C., AND E. S. BUFFA, "A Heurishe Algorithm and Simulation Approach to Relative Location of Facilities," *Management Science*, vol. 9 (Jan., 1963), p. 294.

BARTLETT, C. H., "Considerations in Selecting New Plant Sites," *Electric Light and Power*, Vol. 36, No. 25 (December 15, 1958), p. 73.

BAUMOL, W. J., AND P. WOLFE, "A Warehouse—Location Problem," *The Journal of Operations Research Society of America*, Vol. 6, No. 2 (March–April, 1958), pp. 252–63.

BIERMAN, HAROLD, JR., L. E. FOURAKER, AND R. K. JAEDICKE, *Quantitative Analysis for Business Decisions*. Homewood, Ill.: Richard D. Irwin, Inc., 1961.

BOWKER, A. H., AND G. J. LIEBERMAN, *Engineering Statistics*. Englewood Cliffs, N.J.: Prentice-Hall, Inc., 1959.

BOWMAN, E. H., "Assembly Line Balancing by Linear Programming," *Operations Research*, Vol. 8, No. 3 (May–June, 1960), pp. 385–89.

BOWMAN, E. H., AND ROBERT B. FETTER, *Analysis for Production Management*, rev. ed. Homewood, Ill.: Richard D. Irwin, Inc., 1961.

BUFFA, E. S., *Models for Production and Operations Management*, New York: John Wiley & Sons, Inc., 1963.

BURINGTON, R. S., AND D. C. MAY, JR., *Handbook of Probability and Statistics with Tables*. Sandusky, Ohio: Handbook Publishers, Inc., 1953.

CARSON, G. B. (ed.), *Production Handbook*, 2d ed. New York: The Ronald Press Co., 1958.

CHURCHILL, GILBERT A., JR., "Plant Layout Analysis" (Ph.D. dissertation, Indiana University, 1966).

CRAMER, HAROLD, *Mathematical Methods of Statistics*. Princeton, N.J.: Princeton University Press, 1946.

DUNCAN, ACHESON J., *Quality Control and Industrial Statistics*, rev. ed. Homewood, Ill.: Richard D. Irwin, Inc., 1959.

183

FELLER, W., *An Introduction to Probability Theory and Its Application*, 2d ed. New York: John Wiley & Sons, Inc., 1957.

FETTER, ROBERT B., "Some Application of Probability Theory to Manufacturing Problems," *Industrial Management Reprint No. 26.* Cambridge, Mass.: Massachusetts Institute of Technology.

FLAGLE, C. D., W. H. HUGGINS, AND R. H. ROY, *Operations Research and Systems Engineering.* Baltimore, Md.: The Johns Hopkins Press, 1960.

FORRESTER, GEORGE, "A Statistical Analysis of Some of the Causes of Timed Variance in Stop Watch Studies" (Master's thesis, Georgia Institute of Technology, 1953).

FRASER, D. A. S., *Statistics—An Introduction.* New York: John Wiley & Sons, Inc., 1958.

FROELICH, W. E., "Associate Spring," *Industrial Development*, Vol. 129, No. 3 (March, 1960), p. 15.

GARDINER, DONALD A., "Approximate Variability of Nonlinear Forms," Unpublished Paper.

GOMBERG, WILLIAM, *A Trade Union Analysis of Time Study.* Chicago: Science Research Associates, Inc., 1948.

GRANT, EUGENE L., AND W. GRANT IRESON, *Principles of Engineering Economy*, 4th ed. New York: The Ronald Press Co., 1960.

GREENHUT, M. L., *Plant Location in Theory and Practice.* Chapel Hill, N.C.: University of North Carolina Press, 1956.

HALD, A., *Statistical Theory with Engineering Applications.* New York: John Wiley & Sons, Inc., 1952.

HART, L. W., JR., "Activity Sequencing—A Bibliography," *Journal of Industrial Engineering*, Vol. 14, No. 4 (July–August, 1963), pp. 220–23.

HELD, M., R. M. KARP, AND R. SHARESHIAN, "Assembly Line Balancing—Dynamic Programming with Precedence Constraints," *Operations Research*, Vol. 11, No. 3 (May–June, 1963), pp. 442–59.

HELGESON, W. P., AND D. P. BIRNIE, "Assembly Line Balancing Using the Ranked Positional Weight Technique," *Journal of Industrial Engineering*, Vol. 12, No. 6 (November–December, 1961), pp. 394–98.

HOFFMAN, T. R., "Assembly Line Balancing with a Precedence Matrix," *Management Science*, Vol. 9, No. 4 (July, 1963), pp. 551–63.

HOLMES, W. G., *Plant Location.* New York: McGraw-Hill Book Co., 1930.

"Hotter Bidding for New Plants," *Business Week* (December 16, 1961), pp. 126–30.

HOOVER, EDGAR M., *The Location of Economic Activity.* New York: McGraw-Hill Book Co., 1958.

"How to Choose a Plant Site," *Iron Age*, Vol. 181, No. 13 (March 27, 1958), p. 121.

"How You Can Analyze Standby Equipment Needs," *Plant Engineering* (April, 1959), pp. 111–13.

HU, T. C., "Parallel Sequencing and Assembly Line Problems," *Operations Research*, Vol. 9, No. 6 (November–December, 1961), pp. 841–48.

HUMPHREYS, H. E., JR., "Let's Go Global," *Industrial Development*, Vol. 129, No. 12 (November, 1960), p. 6.

Industrial Location and National Resources. Washington, D.C.: National Resources Planning Board, 1943.

IRESON, WILLIAM G., *Factory Planning and Plant Layout*. New York: Prentice-Hall, Inc., 1952.

ISARD, WALTER, *Location and Space Economy*. New York: John Wiley & Sons, Inc., 1956.

ISARD, WALTER, *Methods of Regional Analysis: An Introduction to Regional Science*. New York: John Wiley & Sons, Inc., 1960.

JACKSON, J. R., "A Computing Procedure for a Line Balancing Problem," *Management Science*, Vol. 2, No. 3 (April, 1956), pp. 261–71.

JOHNSON, ROBERT E., "Application of Linear Programming to Plant Location Decisions," *The Engineering Economist*, Vol. 4, No. 2 (Fall, 1958), pp. 1–16.

KAPLAN, A. D. H., J. B. DIRLAM, AND R. F. LANZILLOTTI, *Pricing in Big Business*. Washington, D.C.: The Brookings Institution, 1958.

KENDALL, M. G., AND A. STUART, *The Advanced Theory of Statistics*, Vol. 1. New York: Hafner Publishing Co., 1958.

KENNEDY, M. H., "An Investigation of the Pattern of Variation of Cycle Performance Times for a Repetitive Manual Operation" (Master's thesis, Georgia Institute of Technology, 1957).

KILBRIDGE, M. D., AND L. WESTER, "A Heuristic Method of Assembly Line Balancing," *Journal of Industrial Engineering*, Vol. 12, No. 4 (July–August, 1961), pp. 292–98.

KIMBALL, D. S., AND D. S. KIMBALL, JR., *Principles of Industrial Organization*. New York: McGraw-Hill Book Co., 1947.

KLEIN, M., "On Assembly Line Balancing," *Operations Research*, Vol. 11, No. 2 (March–April, 1963), pp. 274–81.

KOFF, R. M., "What the Experts Tell Us about Mechanical Reliability," *Product Engineering* (November 16, 1959), pp. 21–24.

KOOPMANS, T. C., AND M. BELKMAN, "Assignment Problems and the Location of Economic Activity," *Econometrica*, Vol. 25 (June, 1957), pp. 53–76.

LLOYD, D. K., AND M. LIPOW, *Reliability: Management, Methods, and Mathematics*. Englewood Cliffs, N.J.: Prentice-Hall, Inc., 1962.

"Location Analysis and Site Selection," *Industrial Development*, Vol. 131, No. 5 (May, 1962), pp. 5–14.

LOSCH, AUGUST, *The Economics of Location*, Trans. W. H. Woglom. New Haven, Conn.: Yale University Press, 1954.

MATHEWSON, MORELEY H., "The Expanding Role of Modern Engineering in Management," *Proceedings of Executive Techniques for Industrial Engineering Conference*. Chicago: Institute for Management Science, 1960, p. 12.

McHOSE, A. H., "A Quadratic Formulation of the Activity Location Problem," *Journal of Industrial Engineering*, Vol. 12, No. 5 (September–October, 1961), pp. 334–37.

METZGER, ROBERT W., *Elementary Mathematical Programming.* New York: John Wiley & Sons, Inc., 1958.

MOOD, A. M., AND F. A. GRAYBILL, *Introduction to the Theory of Statistics,* 2d ed. New York: McGraw-Hill Book Co., 1963.

MOODIE, C. L., AND H. H. YOUNG, "A Heuristic Method of Assembly Line Balancing for Assumptions of Constant or Variable Work Element Times," *Journal of Industrial Engineering,* Vol. 16, No. 1 (January–February, 1965), pp. 23–29.

MOORE, JAMES M., *Plant Layout and Design.* New York: The Macmillan Co., 1962.

MORRIS, WILLIAM T., *Analysis for Materials Handling Management.* Homewood, Ill.: Richard D. Irwin, Inc, 1962.

MORRIS, WILLIAM T., *Engineering Economy.* Homewood, Ill.: Richard D. Irwin, Inc., 1960.

MORRIS, WILLIAM T., "Facilities Planning," *Journal of Industrial Engineering,* Vol. 9, No. 5 (September–October, 1958), pp. 358–61.

MOSES, LEON N., "Location and the Theory of Production," *Quarterly Journal of Economics,* Vol. 73 (May, 1958), pp. 259–72.

MUTHER, RICHARD, *Practical Plant Layout.* New York: McGraw-Hill Book Co., 1955.

NADLER, GERALD, *Work Design.* Homewood, Ill.: Richard D. Irwin, Inc., 1963.

NEWBERRY, T. L., "The Principles and Practices of Industrial Engineering Should Not Necessarily Premise Cost Minimization nor Profit Maximization as Primary Management Criteria" (Ph.D. proposition, Georgia Institute of Technology, 1960).

OSTLE, B., *Statistics in Research,* 2d ed. Ames, Ia.: Iowa State University Press, 1963.

PENUELA, L. J., JR., "An Experimental Evaluation of the Presence of an Analyst on Work Performance Time in Time Study Analysis" (Master's thesis, Georgia Institute of Technology, 1961).

"Plant Site Selection Guide," *Factory Management and Maintenance,* Vol. 119, No. 5 (May, 1957), p. 180.

"Project Feasibility Analysis," *Industrial Development,* Vol. 131, No. 4 (April, 1962), pp. 6–16.

REED, RUDDELL, JR., *Plant Layout: Factors, Principles, and Techniques.* Homewood, Ill.: Richard D. Irwin, Inc., 1961.

REINFELD, NYLES V., AND W. R. VOGEL, *Mathematical Programming.* Englewood Cliffs, N.J.: Prentice-Hall, Inc., 1958.

ROSCOE, E. S., *Organization for Production,* rev. ed. Homewood, Ill.: Richard D. Irwin, Inc., 1959.

RUTTAN, V. W., AND L. T. WALLACE, "Developments in Plant Location Theory," *Industrial Development,* Vol. 130, No. 7 (June, 1961), pp. 57–59.

SALVESON, M. E., "The Assembly Line Balancing Problem," *Journal of Industrial Engineering,* Vol. 6, No. 3 (May–June, 1955), pp. 18–25.

SALVESON, M. E., "The Assembly Line Balancing Problem," *Transactions of the ASME*, Vol. 77 (August, 1955), pp. 939–48.

SCHILLER, D. H., AND M. M. LAVIN, "The Determination of Requirements for Warehouse Dock Facilities," *Operations Research*, Vol. 4 (April, 1956), pp. 231–42.

SHEELE, E. D., W. L. WESTERMAN, AND R. J. WIMMERT, *Principles and Design of Production Control Systems*. Englewood Cliffs, N.J.: Prentice-Hall, Inc., 1960.

SHUBIN, JOHN A., AND HUXLER MADEHEIM, *Plant Layout*. Englewood Cliffs, N.J.: Prentice-Hall, Inc., 1951.

"Site Selection," *Factory*, Vol. 122, No. 5 (May, 1960), p. 197.

"Site Selection," *Factory*, Vol. 123, No. 5 (May, 1961), p. 168.

STUCKEMAN, H. C., "Community Evaluation in Site Selection," *Industrial Development*, Vol. 129, No. 5 (May, 1960), pp. 63–67.

TERBORGH, GEORGE, *Dynamic Equipment Policy*. New York: McGraw-Hill Book Co., 1949.

"The Factors for Expansion Planning," *Industrial Development*, Vol. 129, No. 11 (October, 1960), p. 64.

"The Search for Sites," *Factory*, Vol. 124, No. 5 (May, 1962), p. 185.

THEUSEN, H. G., *Engineering Economy*, 2d ed. Englewood Cliffs, N.J.: Prentice-Hall, Inc., 1957.

THOMPSON, JAMES H., *Methods of Plant Site Selection Available to Small Manufacturing Firms*, West Virginia University Bulletin, Series 62, No. 3–3 (September, 1961).

TONGE, F. M., *A Heuristic Program for Assembly Line Balancing*. Englewood Cliffs, N.J.: Prentice-Hall, Inc., 1961.

TONGE, F. M., "Summary of a Heuristic Line Balancing Procedure," *Management Science*, Vol. 7, No. 1 (October, 1960), pp. 21–42.

"U.S. Round-up—Site Selection Answers from Twelve Top Men," *Factory*, Vol. 122, No. 5 (May, 1960), p. 180.

VASONYI, ANDREW, *Scientific Programming in Business and Industry*. New York: John Wiley & Sons, Inc., 1958.

WADSWORTH, G. P., AND J. G. BRYAN, *Introduction to Probability and Random Variables*. New York: McGraw-Hill Book Co., 1960.

WALLS, R. T., "How to Measure and Control Job Shop Labor Performance," *American Machinist* (October 5, 1959).

WEBER, ALFRED, *Theory of the Location of Industries*, Trans. C. J. Friedrich. Chicago: University of Chicago Press, 1929.

WESTER, L., AND KILBRIDGE, M. D., "Heuristic Line Balancing—A Case," *Journal of Industrial Engineering*, Vol. 13, No. 3 (May–June, 1962), pp. 139–49.

"What Makes a Good Plant Location," *Mill and Factory*, Vol. 65 (July, 1959), p. 67.

WHITE, W. W., "Comments on a Paper by Bowman," *Operations Research*, Vol. 9, No. 2 (March–April, 1961), pp. 274–76.

WILLOUGHBY, DAVID W., "A Technique for Integrating Location and Materials Handling Equipment Selection" (M.S.I.E. thesis, Purdue University, 1967).

WINTERS, P. R., "Forecasting Sales by Exponentially Weighted Moving Averages," *Management Science*, Vol. 6 (1960), pp. 324–42.

YASEEN, LEONARD C., *Plant Location.* New York: American Research Council, 1960.

INDEX

INDEX

*This book has been set in 10 and 9 point Cale-
donia, leaded 2 points. Part numbers are in 24
point Venus Medium Extended. Chapter numbers are in 14 point Venus Medium Extended;
part and chapter titles are in 16 point Venus
Medium Extended. The size of the type page is
27 by 46½ picas.*